DIGITAL LABOR

THE COMING DEMISE
OF THE WHITE-COLLAR WORKER

THOMAS YOUNG

To the White Collar workers who have no idea how fast software
and AI are progressing to take their current jobs

CONTENTS

FOREWORD

IN 1950, Dr. Alan M. Turing, the famous English mathematician, asked the question " ... can machines think?" Since then, computer science and cognitive neuroscience has been on a relentless journey to pursue the answer to this question. As part of this pursuit, in 1998 I left my assistant professorship at NYU and started IPsoft with the goal of creating software that could mimic the human brain. Over the past 20+ years it is incredible to see AI coming closer than ever to positively answering Alan Turing's famous question.

In 2013, I met Tom Young in our offices in New York City and a brief 15-minute meeting turned into a 2-hour discussion on the future of technology, and the impacts of automation and cognitive computing. In the ensuing years, Tom and I had the opportunity to work together, exchange ideas, and become friends. We share a kindred spirit to evangelize the possibilities of working with machines that could truly think. I have found Tom to be one of the most forward and prescient thinkers about the future impact technology will have on our society. From economic impact, to social impact, to impact in the way businesses operate—very little will be untouched by automation and cognitive computing.

In today's marketplace, we are currently seeing a new digital workforce that is transforming the way people and companies interact. IPsoft's cognitive virtual assistant, Amelia, is handling hundreds of thousands of interactions every day through her natural language interface supported by a backend cognitive automation system. We launched the Amelia platform to assist companies by providing them with access to a virtual workforce that can speak to and understand humans through our own natural language. Too often, we adapt to the machines we use every day, but through the advent of artificial intelligence (AI), our machines are now bridging the gap to mirror us. In a sense, Amelia behaves like a service desk agent, but at a fraction of the cost, 24 hours per day, every day. These interactions start out on routine matters but are quickly evolving to more sophisticated interactions as the platform learns and adapts.

As automation and cognitive technologies evolve, we find that the white-collar workforce across many domains is becoming more digital—hence the term Digital Labor. Digital Labor will free us from the mundane aspects of work, disrupting entire industries in the way that machines have previously transformed manufacturing and agriculture. As AI advances further, we will have to rethink the nature of work itself by redefining our own roles in an increasingly automated and intelligent economy. This book lays out the rationale for why the traditional role of the knowledge worker– a white-collar professional who processes information with their brain—will soon be replaced with more efficient and cost-effective cognitive agents like IPsoft's Amelia. This disruption will be profound, and this book is a wakeup call to those who think that their job or business is immune to the coming disruption. Unlike prior automation disruptions in the analog realm, where machines replaced brawn in the manufacturing and agriculture industries, Digital Labor is a multiplier of the brain, and because it is digital, it can scale at machine speed.

The coming digital disruption will have both utopian and dystopian aspects arising from this rapid advancement of Digital Labor displacing traditional labor. I embrace a utopian outlook but believe that in order to achieve these more optimistic outcomes, we all must be more aware of the coming changes and begin the discussion for how we will pivot our society to properly integrate new advancements into our daily lives.

This book is a great place to start. It is not a technical treatise, but rather a philosophical book that encourages the reader to think through the coming implications of automation, cognitive technologies, and Digital Labor as a whole.

I hope you enjoy the read as much as I did.

Chetan Dube
CEO
IPsoft
New York City, July 2019

INTRODUCTION

"The reason why it is so difficult for existing firms to capitalize on disruptive innovations is that their processes and their business model that make them good at the existing business actually make them bad at competing for the disruption."

– Clayton Christensen, author of *Innovator's Dilemma*

IN EARLY 2011, I was working on a very large outsourcing transaction at one of the major Wall Street banks. I was a senior partner at a consulting firm and had worked on billions of dollars of commercial outsourcing contracts and deals over the years. The deal I was working on at the time was not the largest ever, but in 2011, it was the biggest deal in the market at the time. On paper, the deal would have been worth between $4 billion and $5 billion in total contract value.

In the 15 years running up to 2011, I had worked on or had oversight of dozens of commercial contracts in many industries and regions. My colleagues and I used to say we had "seen all of the movies," meaning that when clients would say they were different, we knew better. Cultures and situations had their nuances, but every firm had the same problems in one way or another. Reducing the cost of operations was a common challenge to most firms in every industry sector. Outsourcing these operations to a commercial service provider was a way to get "your mess for less" to meet this challenge.

Meaning, if it costs your firm $100 million to operate a particular function, such as IT, some commercial service providers would agree to do it for much less. As an example, if a firm put out to bid $100 million worth of the firm's IT work, bids could come back from service providers to do the work for $65 to $70 million, saving the firm lots of money every year. This was what was driving the outsourcing industry.

In most cases, these commercial service providers did, in fact, do things for less, but outsourcing was not without its problems. If internal operations were stale, bureaucratic, and expensive, then commercial outsourcing deals were hard to implement, govern, and fully realize the value that was imagined. Most deals ended up saving money, but rarely as much as was anticipated. Typically, outsourcing contracts in those days were a form of labor arbitrage—essentially, shipping high- paying jobs in the US and Europe to India and other geographies with lower labor costs.

Not everyone had the stomach for this kind of work. Some say it was akin to working at a slaughterhouse, but that was not my experience. In most cases, while jobs were certainly impacted in the short-term, broadly speaking, most people ended up in better jobs that were a better fit for them in the long term. There are many examples where someone had a nice-paying job, lost it through outsourcing, and never recovered career-wise. However, most people were able to adapt their skills, get new jobs, and were ultimately better off.

From the late 1990s to 2011, Wall Street was where the action was for the outsourcing of IT operations. Wall Street firms had the biggest IT budgets, the smartest people in the industry, and the highest compensation rates for their IT teams. The financial services industry was also going through a digital revolution that was putting pressure on banks to lower costs and increase performance. This was consulting nirvana and where I spent a good deal of my time.

Most of the Wall Street banks had outsourced a portion of their IT operations and development work. Some, such as JP Morgan, had even insourced work that had been outsourced in prior regimes. I had worked on many of these deals in one way or another and by 2011, I knew my way around.

Anyway, this deal in 2011 signaled that things had begun to change. Up until this point, we could predict with some certainty how much commercial service providers would quote when we put the opportunity to take over IT operations out for bid. The commercial services market for IT at this point was fairly mature and stable. As a result, we could look at comparable outsourcing deals in the marketplace and make an educated assessment—not unlike a real estate appraisal—on what an outsourcing bid would look like for a prospective body of new work.

In 2011, my team did an outsourcing market appraisal for a large bank on its entire IT operations, which was costing the bank about $750 million per year. Because $750 million was larger than most deals at the time, we didn't have many recent deals to compare it to in our database. It was a lot like trying to get an appraisal on a house three times bigger than any house in the area. What is it worth? At some point, it is just a guess. But the answer is: it is worth what the market will bear. Well, the same principle applied to our analysis.

Given the size of this potential deal, my team had to do a number of normalizations, exclusions, and qualifiers that ultimately gave me no confidence in the analysis in the final report. I didn't want to go out to bid without a realistic expectation of what potential bids might be, so I could set the expectation appropriately. So I called a few large commercial service providers who worked at the bank (off the record) and said: "If we put $750 million of annual spending in an outsourcing deal out to bid, how much could you save us?" I could only get a straight answer from service providers because we knew each other and there was some trust. But the answer I got back was that they would bid lower than my team had assessed in our analysis—meaning the savings would be more for the banking client. This was good and I took this information to the CIO of the bank, who agreed to do a formal bid in the market to see what the market would bear.

Once we got the formal bids back, the potential savings if the bank were to outsource the $750 million per year was even greater than my informal phone calls indicated. In fact, the savings were double what was determined by our team's assessment. Ultimately, for many reasons unrelated to savings, this deal was never pursued. However, after 15 years in the industry, I had just seen a new movie.

In the months that followed, I went back to a few of the service providers to find out why our predictive analysis of their bids was so off the mark. The first thing they asked was, "How do you do the analysis? What is your process?" I explained that we use a vast repository of past deals, we normalize pricing and terms, and apply more weight to recent deals to get a sense of the expected bids.

The response from the service providers was, "That is all wrong." Why? Because it had worked in the past, more or less. In 2011, it did not work on this large deal at the bank because service providers had started to augment or replace the offshore labor arbitrage cost model (which had dominated the deals in the prior 10 to 15 years) with automation software. That is, instead of using cheap offshore talent, they were increasingly relying on technology. Since this was the largest deal in the industry at the time, service providers were putting their most aggressive and innovative solutions on the table to win. Looking in the rearview mirror was no longer a good indicator of the road ahead, which came as a significant wake-up call to me as an industry veteran.

Over the next few years, I looked more deeply into the notion of software replacing complex labor in IT services, and then more broadly at the impact on general business functions like finance and customer service. In 2013, this led me to start Rumjog Enterprises, which is a small boutique consulting firm focused on how advanced software and emerging technologies would change the way work was done. It would ultimately change the outsourcing industry where I spent a good deal of my career, as well.

When I first started talking about this coming technology transformation at conferences and seminars, people were not buying into the concept. I was challenging some of the norms in the industry.

No one thinks that now.

Advanced software and automation are in full stride, disrupting everything from IT services to finance work, HR work, customer service, as well as many other forms of white-collar work.

While people see the impact of advanced software and automation on the industry today, most people, even industry insiders, do not appreciate the scope and breadth of where this is heading. **It is completely underestimated**.

In the last few years, I have been relatively shocked that more people have not recognized what is coming with respect to Digital Labor and the automation of white-collar work. You need only spend some time studying what is happening in AI and machine learning in order to appreciate the significant impact that Digital Labor will have on future job markets and the way we do business.

This book is not written for industry insiders. Many industry insiders are vested in the current models, and major disruptions from technology are difficult for some to embrace. The quote at the beginning of this introduction from Clayton Christensen gets to the heart of it. This book is written for everyone, not necessarily people who are in the technology industry. This book is for those who have an interest in the coming impact that technology will have on their lives, their livelihoods, and the world around them. Meaning, virtually everyone.

There are certainly dystopian aspects to this topic, which we discuss. However, it should also be noted that there are plenty of positive aspects, or utopian outcomes, to technological change as well. It is my hope that you will focus your energy on taking advantage of the many positive opportunities that will emerge to enhance your life, the lives of your family, friends, colleagues, and our society as a whole.

PART I:

Current State of Affairs

CHAPTER 1:

What Is Digital Labor?

"We always overestimate the change that will occur in the next two years and underestimate the change that will occur in the next ten. Don't let yourself be lulled into inaction."

- Bill Gates in *The Road Ahead*, 1995

IN 2004, Blockbuster was the 800-pound gorilla of the video and DVD rental industry. It generated $5.9 billion in annual revenue supported by 60,000 employees and was *the* place to which consumers turned if they were in the mood to watch a movie from the comforts of home. The walls of Blockbuster's 9,000 stores were lined with small boxes featuring images of the latest movies available for rent, at the going rate of around $4 per night. Customers could also stock up on popcorn, drinks, and other snacks at inflated prices. And everyone who didn't return their movie on time was subject to a late fee that generated approximately 16 percent of Blockbuster's total revenue[1] in 2000, or just under $800 million, the Associated Press reported.

While they accounted for only a small percent of Blockbuster's total revenue, the company's hefty late fees were what later caused the company's demise. In fact, 1997 was the beginning of the end for Blockbuster. That was the year that customer Reed Hastings was charged a $40 late fee by Blockbuster for taking too long to finish watching *Apollo 13*.[2] Annoyed by the fine and the inconvenience of having to go to a store to return the video, he began to conceive of a movie-rental business without late fees or even the need to travel to a retailer.

Netflix, as the new business was named, offered free shipping and returns of any movie in its inventory by mail for a mere $20 a month. Starting with a library of just 925 movies on DVD, the company grew quickly.

At around the same time as Netflix was expanding, Redbox movie-rental kiosks began popping up inside supermarkets and convenience stores, offering one-night rentals of physical DVDs for only $1. This put price pressure on Blockbuster that it hadn't faced previously. It gradually cut its rental price to $1 to compete, slashing its revenue in the process. But the real pressure was coming from Netflix.

After struggling for a few years early on with the shipping and management of physical DVDs, Netflix transformed the movie industry with its streaming-video service. First, it partnered with Starz in 2008 to offer streaming alongside its movie-delivery-by-mail service. By 2011, it had jettisoned the mailed-DVD side of the business and went all-in on digital streaming. Then in 2013, it again zigged when the industry zagged and began introducing its own original content, first with *House of Cards,* to distinguish the company from new competitors offering streaming-movie rentals.

In 2014, Blockbuster filed for bankruptcy a second time (the first was in 2010) and closed its doors for good. Netflix, meanwhile, continues to grow. In 2019, Netflix had a market capitalization of $150 billion—30 times what Blockbuster's was in its heyday—and annual revenue of $17.5 billion, all with zero brick-and-mortar stores and 7,000 employees—10 percent of the workforce Blockbuster had required to run its corporate enterprise.

It took 13 years for Netflix to cause Blockbuster such irreparable damage that it was forced to declare bankruptcy in 2010. Thirteen years might sound like a lot of time to completely transform an industry, but the reality is that more of these stories are emerging—stories of industry upheaval, corporate bankruptcy, and job elimination—at an ever-quickening pace. Going forward, such wide-scale change will happen in months or weeks, not years.

The tipping point for Netflix was its use of software, which it used initially to determine how many of which physical DVDs to buy and where to locate the service centers it used to ship out the discs. Once it shifted to streaming videos, it relied on software algorithms to recommend movies to customers, based on what they had rented previously.

Analog versus Digital

Blockbuster's history is a prime example of analog technology being replaced by digital. The shift from analog to digital is essentially the shift from physical products to virtual ones, as in movies on videotape and DVD to movies streamed digitally. Music also used to be analog, when it was recorded and stored on vinyl discs, then 8-track tapes, cassettes, followed by CDs. Then it was converted to digital music, first sold individually as albums and songs through iTunes or shared through peer-to-peer networks such as Napster, and then sold via streaming services such as Apple Music and Spotify.

Industry leader Spotify currently makes available more than 30 million songs, with 20,000 new songs added to the platform daily. It has over 200 million active users and 100 million users who pay $9.99 per month for its premium service. The ten-year-old company generates $6 billion in revenue annually and currently has a $26 billion valuation.

It is also changing how music is purchased and enjoyed. Rather than paying $18 for a whole album of music, customers now pick and choose individual songs they want to own, through platforms like Apple's iTunes, or they pay a streaming service for access to all the songs out there. This à-la-carte preference is now pushing musicians to produce and release individual songs, rather than entire albums consisting of several songs.

Interestingly, most record labels now receive as much as 80 percent of their revenue from streaming. Warner Music Group[3] has stated publicly that streaming is its main source of revenue, while other labels have reported huge jumps in revenue from streaming.

Where digital music sounded the death knell of albums and record stores, Wikipedia wiped out *Encyclopedia Britannica*, and digital cameras bankrupted Kodak. These are not isolated examples. There are numerous industries and companies that are facing threats from digital technologies. However, the shift from analog to digital generally follows the same path. The digitization of content allows for and ultimately leads to "as a service" being the primary delivery model. As more work becomes digitized, more as-a-service companies will spring up. Just look at freelance marketplaces like Fiverr, where marketing and writing tasks start at $5, Upwork, where freelance writers can connect with clients, and Topcoder, a marketplace for software developers.

The Quickening Pace of Change

The evolution from analog to digital is made possible to a large degree through the automation of analog labor—of tasks humans have historically performed. Broadly speaking, automation is the use of technology to replace human effort, it effectively reduces the need for humans to perform manual work.

More than 300 years ago humans lived in a primarily agrarian society where work was centered on growing crops to support inhabitants. Land was prepared, seeds planted, crops harvested, and fruits and vegetables processed all by hand, with the help of horses and other livestock. Raw materials like cotton and wool were woven into textiles on manual spinning wheels. But thanks to an 18th century invention in England, spinning became automated. Thanks to automation, humans were needed to a much lesser extent to manufacture textiles. The invention of the steam and combustion engine further led to the mechanization of farm work and transportation.

These technologies led to the dawn of the industrial age, during which machines were designed to handle more aspects of manufacturing, freeing workers to explore other industries and skills. For the next 100 years, the industrial age led to impressive advancements in automation and the mechanization of production processes.

The second industrial age, which lasted about 50 years—half the length of the industrial age—was a continuation of the automation of tasks, but the focus shifted to science and technology developments. It was the age of the assembly line and improved manufacturing productivity, which created great wealth. Combined with the expansion of transportation and communication methods, the second industrial age fueled the rapid adoption of technological advances.

Those advances led to the information age of the late 20th century, which made possible incredible advances in computing technology. In a matter of 30 years, computers shrank in size from filling rooms to sitting on a desktop to residing in a handheld phone and increased in processing power hundreds of times over. The more powerful computers became, the quicker they became superior at completing tasks formerly assigned to workers.

The nature of work began to shift, some jobs became obsolete thanks to new software programs, while new jobs emerged in response to the rising use of computing technology. Roles requiring advanced skills were created, such as software developers, engineers, website designers, and social media managers, to name a few jobs that didn't exist 20 years ago, while jobs requiring fewer, or less-specialized skills, faded away.

Now that we are well into the digital age, the concept of automation has evolved. The economy is rapidly morphing, as computer software has advanced to the point to where it can program itself, making decisions faster than humans, and evolving on its own. In many cases, humans are not needed to design programs or even, in some cases, to code. The software can do it on its own. Where prior ages witnessed machines replacing human muscle, we have entered an age where brain power is being automated, and at a pace that is ever-quickening. This is digital automation, which is different from physical automation, and the impacts to human work will be focused on automating brainwork, commonly known as knowledge work.

The role that humans play in knowledge work is going through a polar shift of sorts, where instead of knowledge workers being supported by technology, expert engineers are supporting the technology that is now performing the work.

The Rise of Digital Labor

The phrase Digital Labor is meant to embody the concept of advanced software and platforms performing knowledge work (i.e., work that requires brain processing) that we have typically associated being performed by humans. Digital Labor has been around for decades—think operator-assisted switchboards giving way to fully automated call routing—but we are now at a point of inflection that will see the Digital Labor trend accelerate exponentially. Whether we realize it or not, Digital Labor is more pervasive in the workplace than we may recognize.

One example is the autopilot feature on airplanes, which has been in use for many years. Modern commercial aircraft can take off, fly, interact with flight control, and land without any action taken by the pilot. However, for the most part, pilots take off and land the plane, and they use the plane's autopilot for more than 90 percent of the flight. Human intervention is rarely needed.

While autopilot is a fairly well-known example, the dramatic changes in high-frequency stock trading may not be. Where human traders used to fill the floors of stock exchanges, buying and selling stocks on behalf of clients, today those floors are silent. Trading floors and human traders themselves have all but been eliminated, replaced by software-based platforms that operate at hyper speed.

In the last 15 years, a significant portion of the financial-services jobs involving trading in New York City have been eliminated or shifted into new sectors within financial services, such as equity traders, risk analysts, fund managers, research, and other job functions. These types of positions are being rapidly replaced by technology.

Goldman Sachs's U.S. cash equities trading desk[4] is a prime example of the job shifts that are already under way. In 2000, the major Wall Street banks, like Goldman Sachs and Morgan Stanley, employed thousands of well-paid traders, who could earn up to $500,000 per year or more to trade stocks on behalf of the firms. Nearly twenty years later, most of these trading jobs have been eliminated through high frequency trading (HFT). HFT is a software-based trading platform that requires no human intervention to operate. The HFT platforms cost less and make more for the banks.

Until recently, we have not seen the broad disruptive impact of this elimination or shift because the financial service sector and the economy had the capacity to absorb these displaced workers without a visible impact. The former workers, earning six- and seven-figure salaries and bonuses, spent money on luxury apartments, wardrobes, entertainment and dining, travel, and transportation, among many other things. During bonus week, exotic car dealers would line Wall Street with high-end sports cars and sell Lamborghinis and Porsches on the spot.

Replacing these highly compensated equity traders were engineers who could operate the HFT platforms and a few "quants," or numbers people, who could program the algorithms for trading. These engineers and "quants" are now being replaced with autonomous platforms and AI leveraging machine learning to determine trading protocols.

As the trading floor that was once filled with desks and highly compensated traders have been replaced by open space filled only with the quiet hum of computer servers handling the trades, the ripple effects in the industry extended beyond the trading floors. Without those well-paying financial industry jobs, there has been a steep drop-off in trading support services, real estate occupancy, staff, computer support teams, and other ancillary services that existed to keep the trading floor operating. Not to mention the decline in Lamborghini sales during bonus week, which is almost nonexistent; computers don't need bonuses.

Software platforms don't need the level of support that humans did, and some companies have spotted the opportunity. Virtu Financial is one.

Started by Vincent Viola, Virtu Financial, based in New York City, has a market capitalization of around $4 billion and only about 480 employees. Prior to going public, Virtu Financial had a nearly flawless trading record, with 1,277 up days out of 1,278 trading days. That's impressive. High-frequency trading represents one of the most advanced deployments of automation technologies in the marketplace. The automation has gone well beyond performing human functions, to executing actions that could only be done by machines—e.g., buying and selling multiple times per second. As high-frequency trading evolved, the trading platforms were able to use big data analytics and machine learning to predict future trends in the market. How else do you have 1,277 out of 1,278 up days?

The Multiple Forms of Digital Labor

The examples of Digital Labor are not limited to the financial services industry. There are many, many examples. In order to fully appreciate the impact across all types of knowledge work in every industry, it is important to understand that there are multiple types of Digital Labor. Digital Labor solutions have emerged based on the technology available, starting with simple single task automation to task orchestration to well-developed and complex artificial intelligence. The current forms of Digital Labor include:

- **Task automation**. A single task formerly performed manually can be made automatic. Examples include a car's cruise-control function or the word-count feature in word-processing software. Now instead of counting each word on a typed page, you can pull down a menu and the program will tell you automatically how many words are on the page, or in the highlighted passage.

- **Task orchestration**. When you have multiple tasks to be completed in concert, such as the process of printing and folding brochures and attaching mailing labels to each, tasks are being orchestrated (think of an orchestra with multiple instruments being coordinated simultaneously). Tabulating and analyzing hundreds of survey responses is another example of task orchestration.

- **Incorporating environmental data**. When the automation platforms begin to incorporate data about the environment they are operating in, the automation can adapt dynamically to the conditions without human intervention.

This can be done in either of two ways: through a reactive or predictive approach.

- **Reactive Approach**—A simple example is attaching a sensor to a traffic light to determine when the light needs to change, based on which lanes are most occupied. A more advanced example is using facial-recognition cameras in a retail setting, and automatically adjusting lighting conditions and sales strategies based on the gender, mood, and social score of the people in the store to maximize sales and profit for the retailer. This advanced example is on the cutting edge of retail, but expect to see this sooner rather than later as brick-and-mortar stores try to compete with online shopping that already uses social profiles in e-commerce. To get a fuller sense of the deployment of social scores, go to Netflix and watch *Black Mirror,* Season 3 Episode 1, titled "Nosedive." This episode gives a somewhat dystopian outlook on this topic, but it is meant to be a thought-provoking lens into a possible future. The episode shows when we take social media to an extreme and not only rate but are rated on every interaction. If you are an Uber car-service user, you can see your social score today within the app settings. Your score is used in conjunction with driver scores to determine how fast and often you can get a ride.

- **Predictive Approach (more advanced)**—A familiar example here is the Google autonomous car. Sensors on the Google car record more than 1 million pieces of information per second to assist the car in making complex decisions by itself, such as making a left-hand turn in traffic. Sensors can map the environment and predict potential hazards, then take corrective action before there is a problem.

- **Artificial Intelligence.** Artificial intelligence by itself is a very broad topic, and it stands at the pinnacle of Digital Labor. The most common deployment of artificial intelligence in Digital Labor deployments is artificial neural networks (ANNs). ANNs use the same construct as the human brain to process information and environmental inputs, but at machine speed and scale. Most examples of ANNs are quite complex, but the most straightforward example would be in computer image recognition, where a computer is asked if a certain picture is of a ball or a cat. Historically, we would try to program the rules for what a ball is, and the rules for what a cat is. The computer would then run those rules against the image to provide an answer to the question. The program that made this possible required a lot of human programming and complex rule sets, to account for all the variations among both balls and cats. This is not how ANNs work. ANNs can "learn" through examples—millions and millions of examples—of what is a ball and what is a cat. As it learns, the ANN encodes itself to be able to quickly identify what is a ball and what is a cat after being exposed to many examples. This process of learning through many examples versus following a set of pre-defined rules is called *deep learning*.

  Although there are many forms of Digital Labor, they often work together, and the end result is essentially the same: software programs can accomplish tasks that humans used to, often better and faster.

Most experts argue that increasing automation is ultimately good for humans, freeing them to spend time on other, higher value, activities. The truth is more nuanced. Historically and generally speaking, these technologies have been a net positive for human labor. However, we will reach a point where automation software is doing an increasing majority of work that humans formerly performed, making it increasingly difficult for people to find meaningful jobs. Further, the speed and acceleration of the automation transformation will make it even more difficult for people to be retrained and adjust their skills to the ever-shrinking employment market.

Companies are already taking steps to significantly reduce their work-forces, and to re-skill and recruit for jobs of the future (albeit in many cases, fewer jobs). The new jobs being created will demand skills that require a level of education and intelligence that do not exist universally in today's workforce. Some workers will flourish in this new world; most will not.

Job Enhancers Become Job Killers

The conveniences and productivity boosters of today are actually the job killers of tomorrow. While in most industries we have only some of the components in place to achieve full automation, we are quickly getting to the point that software will assume many of the roles that humans once did.

Let's look at the transportation industry, and more specifically truck drivers. Below is a graphic, showing the most common job in each state. Each year, the data shifts somewhat, but truck driver is one of the most prevalent job categories across the US. Driverless cars and driverless trucks are being road tested in several markets. Once these road tests can prove that automated vehicles perform at a much higher level than human drivers, both from an efficiency and a safety perspective, how fast will the graphic below change? When these truck drivers are displaced by driverless vehicles, what jobs will they be qualified for and capable of doing in the emerging economy? Will they make more money, or less money? How much will it cost to re-train them? Is it even possible? How long will this re-training take? How long will they be unemployed?

These are the questions we will be exploring in further detail throughout this book.

Most Common Job by State

Source: IPUMS-CPS/ University Of Minnesota

Waves of Change

These various forms of Digital Labor will come in successive waves, impacting to a greater and greater degree how work gets done. And the waves that are coming are unpredictable. The future is not an extrapolation of the past—it's very different. That makes it hard to anticipate and plan for.

Elon Musk has said that transportation will be the first industry to be wiped out. And from the previous graphic, this industry provides the most jobs in most states. Given that Tesla has already installed software that provides considerable driver support to Tesla owners, we are likely several years out from a true driverless car.

All the technologies that lead to the driverless vehicle comprise the first Digital Labor wave in this industry. Uber has already stated that it will buy all the driverless cars being produced, which means that the need for individuals to own cars will dramatically decline. In the next decade, it's possible that people will no longer own their own cars.

In the second wave of change, there will be consequential impacts to businesses that are linked to private car ownership. With fewer people owning cars, there will be fewer car dealerships, fewer gas stations, fewer mechanics, fewer car washes, and fewer car insurance policies, among other things. Beyond business impacts, without a need for a car in the garage, new home designs will emerge, and the need for parking in urban areas will change dramatically.

In the third wave of change, we will see entirely new business models emerge. Entrepreneurs will deliver products and services in conjunction with new forms of transportation to take advantage of drivers becoming passengers.

Additionally, the time between each wave will grow successively smaller. Once the driverless car is readily available and can be summoned via Uber, sales of new and used traditional cars will drop precipitously. The fall of supporting industries—the dealerships and gas stations—will take less time, and as acceptance of driverless cars rises, home designs will quickly change course, and finally new business models will rapidly emerge as soon as these changes happen.

Each successive wave will have a greater impact on the structure of how work gets done. The direct loss of jobs is often accompanied by an even greater *indirect* loss of jobs and support personnel that expands with each successive wave.

Digital Labor will irrevocably change our labor markets and the need not only for human workers, but for knowledge workers. Knowledge workers earn their pay by using their brains to solve problems and are particularly vulnerable to Digital Labor technologies.

The elimination of knowledge work isn't the next thing; it's a different thing. It's not incremental change; it's exponential. The pace at which it's going to happen is revolutionary—faster than you'd ever expect. In fact, tens of thousands of jobs have already been wiped out, and more are on the horizon.

The level of automation we're talking about here is the automation of brain work, not physical work, which is quite different from past eras. That puts jobs at all levels of the organization at risk of eventual replacement by machines and software, including those requiring critical-thinking skills. In the next chapter, we'll cover how, exactly, that's happening.

CHAPTER 2:

Knowledge Worker Automation

"How did you go bankrupt?"
"Two ways. Gradually, and then suddenly."

- Ernest Hemingway, *The Sun Also Rises*

WE'VE HEARD NEWS REPORTS of the looming end of unskilled labor due to technology advances, but much less has been said about knowledge work—work that requires brain power, not muscle power. Knowledge workers are engineers, doctors, architects, scientists, accountants, and lawyers. They are educated professionals who have spent many years learning their crafts or acquiring skills necessary to do their jobs.

Unfortunately, today, the pace of technology change exceeds our pace of learning. Humans can't keep up—even highly skilled, educated ones. We're no match for technology's capacity to learn at light speed.

Technologies impacting the workflow and automation of knowledge workers are progressing at an exponential rate. This accelerating pace makes it extremely difficult to keep up with the changes affecting knowledge work. Industries and markets are being transformed. Yet too few people recognize the monumental shift underway. Thanks to normalcy bias, we assume that the changes we're witnessing are much like the gradual and incremental changes we've experienced in the past. We assume, or have a paradigm, that the pace of change is and will always be linear, it will not.

With this linear paradigm, we make faulty assumptions about the consequences of the coming disruptive changes. Normal innovations follow a linear curve while disruptive innovations like Digital Labor follow a non-linear curve. Specifically, normal innovations make incremental improvements to the way things are done. Tomorrow is like yesterday, just slightly better. However, disruptive innovations, make tomorrow very different from yesterday—it is transformational. The difference in this context is like the difference between lightning and lightning bug.

So, what's different about Digital Labor and the automation of knowledge work that makes it disruptive and non-linear?

The Automation of Knowledge Work

First off, there is nothing new about the concept of automation. It's the application of automation itself that has evolved due to technology.

As mentioned in Chapter 1, as a society we experienced automation in both the agricultural and manufacturing economies. We started as a nation of farmers and through automation innovation, now only a small amount of the workforce remains as farmers. The automation of farm work with machines drove a percentage of the workforce in the 90th percentile to less than 2 percent, as shown in the following graph.

Farm Jobs, % of Total U.S Jobs 1790 to 2018

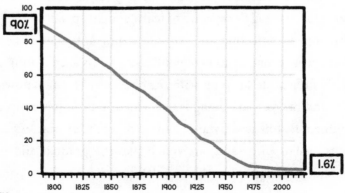

Sources: USDA, BLS

With industrial automation, the impact was more immediate than in farming, but changes still took three decades. US manufacturing jobs peaked in 1980 and dropped more than 35 percent by 2010, while output doubled, as shown in the following graph.

US Real Manufacturing Output vs Employment, 1947 to 2018

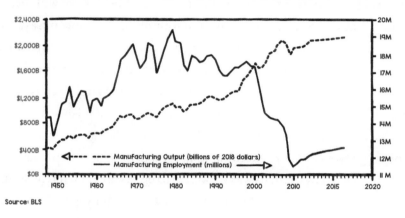

Source: BLS

Both of these labor automation trends can be described as analog transformations—analog in the sense that the human worker was replaced by a physical machine: a tractor, a harvester, a packaging machine, or a spray-painting robot, for example. In both of these labor automation trends—agricultural and industrial—change manifested over decades, thereby establishing our collective paradigm for future automation trends. In other words, experience has taught us to believe that it takes time, measured in years, for these automation trends to impact the ecosystem.

The Rise of Digital Automation

Although we may expect that knowledge-worker automation will follow a similar trend as in the agriculture and manufacturing industries, it won't. It won't because knowledge-worker automation leveraging Digital Labor is not analog, so it will have very different characteristics. It will have characteristics that resemble digital economies rather than analog economies. What are these characteristics? In the book *The Zero Marginal Cost Society: The Internet of Things, the Collaborative Commons, and the Eclipse of Capitalism*, Jeremy Rifkin talks about digital products and services that have a zero or near-zero marginal cost to produce. This trend to zero changes the economic landscape and deployment of products and services.

At Rumjog, we call this the Rumjog Zero Concept, which we will discuss in more detail in Chapter 3. Essentially, the Rumjog Zero Concept says that we will see an accelerating trend towards zero costs, zero cycle times, and zero defects for products and services as the services become more digital. The closer we get to zero, the less room there is for labor. Why? Because labor costs money, labor takes time to execute, and people make mistakes.

The characteristics of Digital Labor allow us to challenge the assumption that knowledge workers were immune to automation because the logic and thought process used by humans was viewed as irreplaceable. That is no longer the case. Rapid advances in hardware and software computing technologies, big data and analytics, machine learning, and artificial intelligence (AI)—all digital technologies—have led to the early stages of knowledge-worker automation. Because these technologies are digital and not analog, they will progress very differently in the economy.

In summary, knowledge-worker-automation trend is a digital transformation trend, in contrast to the prior automation trends (see table below):

Sector	Automation Trend
Agriculture	Analog
Manufacturing	Analog
Knowledge Workers	Digital

What is different about digital? Speed, scale, economics, quality, and impacts to the ecosystem—basically, everything. Applying our prior experiences with labor automation from the agriculture and manufacturing sectors leads us in the wrong direction.

Here's another way to examine the difference:

- Analog: Physical machines
- Digital: Software

Applying this perspective, let's look at speed and scale first. In the digital realm, once a solution to replace a category of knowledge work is developed, it can scale almost instantly across the ecosystem. Why? Because it is software-based and not tied to the physical deployment of machines as replacements for workers. There is no limit to scaling or replicating software in the same sense that there is in building physical machines subject to the constraints of a physical supply chain.

What about economics and quality in the digital realm? Think zero: zero incremental cost and zero defects. Not literally zero, but close to it, compared to analog counterparts.

The Impact of Labor Automation on the Ecosystem

When automation of labor impacted farms in the agricultural transformation, reducing opportunities, workers migrated from rural areas to urban to pursue new manufacturing jobs created by the Industrial Revolution. The pace of change, while disruptive to individuals and families, was, relatively speaking, manageable for society as a whole. In fact, most economists would argue the change was, ultimately, a net benefit to society and led to a better standard of living for all. For example, back-breaking lettuce picking once performed by agriculture workers is increasingly done by automated lettuce harvesters[5]. However, the standard of living for agricultural workers who lost their jobs due to automation and failed to shift their skillsets has seen a relative decline compared to industrial workers.

When the automation of manufacturing labor began, the pace of change of industrialization occurred much faster than in the past, and many affected workers had difficulty finding employment at the same compensation levels. This forced many into lower-paying jobs in the service sector, lowering their standard of living. A minority of the workers had the skills, education, and capability to perform the residual jobs left in the wake of automation. Further, the standard of living for industrial workers who lost their jobs due to automation has been flat or in decline relative to the standard of living of knowledge workers.

The speed and scale of the knowledge-worker transformation of labor will reduce workers' standard of living following future labor market shifts. Some knowledge workers—a minority—will have the education and ability to shift into new job markets. However, the majority will simply be out of a job. How many people? McKinsey Global Institute estimates that by the year 2030, approximately 400 million workers globally could be impacted by this trend.

The knowledge-worker labor-automation trend will be too fast for society to make adjustments in the same way that society adjusted to the agricultural and industrial revolutions. The people and institutions that make up our society take time to understand the changes and adapt to the new realities of the market. It took decades to go from the one-room schoolhouse serving the agrarian society to the K-12 assembly-line format serving the industrial economy.

Believing the future will look a lot like the past is kind of like looking in the rear-view mirror to determine how you drive. If you're on a long, straight road, you can probably get away with this for a while; however, on a curving road, representing a non-linear market, you're most likely to end up in a ditch, or worse.

We recognize the pace of change is accelerating, so we should not be applying the old rules to the future in the same way we shouldn't drive our car using the rear-view mirror. Our point of view cannot be "the road ahead looks an awful lot like what's behind us." The road ahead is quite different.

What's Different about Digital Labor?

Yes, for the next few years, things will look much the same. We will continue to see productivity improvements due to increasingly automated work processes. Lower-level jobs—such as customer-service agents or clerical workers—will slowly be phased out here and there. We will see a progression of job replacement with software followed by massive cuts in a variety of industries. Jobs at all skill levels will be impacted, and very few job classifications will be secure.

Right now, there are several programs being tested and deployed in every sector of the market, to see how far automation can be pushed. As confidence builds in the automation deployments, we will see an accelerating pace of knowledge-worker job elimination. The perceived impact feels slow now, but when it becomes more visible, it will be sudden.

Amelia: The First Digital Employee?

When Swedish bank SEB (*Skandinaviska Enskilda Banken* AB) announced in October 2016 that it had hired its first digital employee, the news didn't attract much attention. And yet this was perhaps the first time a company had officially acknowledged the increasingly important role Digital Labor is playing.

SEB's newest employee, Amelia, represented by a blonde-haired avatar in a navy-blue suit and button-down shirt, is a cognitive agent, or a software program that can mimic human interactions.

Image of Amelia courtesy of IPsoft.

Its creators at IPsoft call her an AI-based virtual digital assistant, or VDA. What makes Amelia distinctive is that she can think and act much like humans, including learning from each situation.

Despite how complex our virtual agents may seem to have become, cracking the code on a technology that can learn human language has remained a distant target. Cognitive chatbots have a long way to go, but hints of their eventual impact on the market can already be felt.

Amelia began as a pilot program for SEB's internal help desk in September 2015. During the first three weeks she was deployed, she reportedly participated in more than 4,000 conversations with 700 employees, according to Rasmus Järborg, SEB's chief strategy officer, and she was able to solve the bulk of the issues almost immediately. Having proven successful with an internal audience, Amelia began taking care of front-line customer-service interactions by December of that same year. Those responsibilities included opening accounts, issuing bank cards, scheduling meetings, and disseminating branch office information.

Within one year, Amelia was able to handle 15 percent of all help-desk calls without human intervention. And she could have handled more. However, SEB had designed her to escalate calls to humans quickly "rather than frustrate their employees ... SEB restrained Amelia by design," according to the report "Service Automation: Cognitive Virtual Agents at SEB Bank." When left to her own devices, Amelia can handle more than 60 percent of client requests without human intervention, with a 90 percent+ accuracy rate and 88 percent customer satisfaction rating on most factors, reports "IPsoft's Amelia: More than a chatbot," a publication prepared by London-based analysis and research firm Ovum.

While SEB, with the help of its IT partner IPsoft, is on the leading edge of adopting cognitive agents, it is not the only financial institution dipping its toes into the automation of knowledge work. UBS and insurer VGZ[6] are said to also be deploying cognitive agents.

The Difference Between Cognitive Agents and Chatbots

So, isn't Amelia just another chatbot variation? Actually, no, she's not. Amelia is very different in some key ways—differentiators that spotlight the gains that have been made in artificial intelligence.

Chatbots support companies by searching for keywords and responding to them with a matching pre-programmed response. They are most commonly used on retail websites, providing pre-written answers to frequently asked questions in real time, or as part of customer-service operations, asking questions to determine who the customer should speak with live. Chatbots have a finite library of keywords that they use to match with the appropriate response—they have been programmed to simulate human conversation, but the capability for episodic memory functions, learning from interactions, and understanding natural language simply doesn't exist. Chatbots don't store or recall dialogue. According to Ovum's report, they are more like examples of robotic process automation (RPA, which perform repeatable, rules-based tasks, often in back-office situations) than a more advanced form of artificial intelligence.

The iPhone's Siri, in its current form, is primarily a chatbot. Siri responds with pre-programmed information based on keywords. However, for the most part, Siri does not build new responses based on prior conversations. What do we mean by this? At Rumjog, we developed a simple cognitive test (see Turing Test below) to determine if a chatbot truly understands what you are saying to it. Run this test against Siri and you'll understand Siri's current limitations. You could run the same test with Amazon's Alexa and other chat agents and you will get similar results. Now, we say this with some level of reservation because things are changing as we type.

The Turing Test

In fact, chatbots are edging closer to being indistinguishable from humans in interactions—to be able to pass the Turing Test. Today there are five groups technologies that go into making a chatbot function in a way that mimics human communication:

1. Voice-to-text
2. Text-to-understanding
3. Decision engine
4. Natural language production
5. Text-to-voice

Each of these technology groups leverages a myriad of individual components to play their part in the delivery of service, all of which happens in near real-time.

A chatbot can eliminate voice-to-text and text-to-voice use because the interaction between human and computer is in text form, not voice.

The most challenging technology groups is group 2: Text-to-understanding.

Text-to-understanding is the Holy Grail in the broad field of AI. If computers can truly understand us, how far are we from computers that are sentient and have personalities?

Rumjog developed a series of tests to determine whether a chatbot or interactive system has "cracked" the elusive text-to-understanding puzzle.

The tests are simple conceptually, but extremely difficult for computers to process, especially at scale.

Test 1: Simple Test

- Statement 1: *I have five apples.*
- Statement 2: *I gave an apple to a friend.*

- First Question: *How many apples do I have left?*
- Second Question: *How many people have fruit?*

This test reveals whether the chatbot can process simple information into a framework (a neurological ontology) and then recall and process that information without a reliance on keywords. Concepts of nouns, verbs, and possession are required to be understood and modified as new information is provided (e.g., *I gave an apple to a friend*).

This is a simple test that you would expect a 5-year-old to be able to answer, but very few chatbots can handle.

Test 2: Context-Switching Test

- Statement 1: *I have five apples.*
- Statement 2: *Steve gave me a ride to work today, but I needed to get a ride home from someone else*
- Statement 3: *I gave an apple to Steve.*
- Statement 4: *Mary gave me a ride home after work today.*

- First Question: *How many apples do I have left?*
- Second Question: *Who drove me home from work today?*
- Third Question: *How many people have fruit?*

This test introduces context-switching. In order for a computer to be able to process the information and recall it in context, the statements must be processed into proper context. The apples are in a different ontological branch than the work transportation. The information must be ingested and stored into the proper location in order to be able recall and answer simple questions.

The test is fairly straightforward, but it becomes difficult at scale. Also, most chatbots today simply react to the prior sentence; they do not build out a library of experience and get more sophisticated over time. There is no recall.

Test 3: Language-Switching Test

- Statement 1: *I have five apples.*
- Statement 2: *Ich habe einem Freund einen Apfel gegeben.* (German)

- First Question: *Combien de pommes me reste-t-il?* (French)
- Second Question: ¿Cuántas personas tienen fruta? (Spanish)

This test is identical to Test 1, except that a different language is used in the statements and questions. If someone were multi-lingual, this would be no problem for a simple test like this. However, this test is very difficult to encode in a computer system and reveals the use of keywords to emulate understanding.

Test 4: Language and Context

You can combine Tests 2 and 3 to come up with even more complex tests to see how well the chatbot truly understands the language and interaction.

It may be surprising to people that such simple tests are difficult to encode in a system. At issue is the ability for the software to encode experience into understanding, in real time, without human intervention. That is, you can teach a system that your name is John, but that is a structured learning or a feature versus dynamic unstructured learning.

Many firms are working to crack this problem. Machine learning and artificial neural networks are at the heart of these emerging solutions. When these systems can start to learn with us, share experiences, and recall those experiences, we will move into a new relationship with the software and platforms that we work with.

Now, when you run the Rumjog cognitive test against IPSoft's Amelia, you get very different results because Amelia goes well beyond simple parroting of information.

Amelia deconstructs the language into a neural framework similar to the way a human brain does. She then "understands" the content of the dialogue. As Amelia interacts, the software program builds that experience into the neural framework and is able to recall this knowledge. She "learns."

Reports IPsoft, "Amelia understands the underlying meaning of your statements and can engage in fluid conversations. As she detects a customer's mood, she is able to adapt the content of her responses and associated expressions to create a truly personal experience."

Cognitive agents are more intelligent than chatbots, which are fairly simple software programs that can ask and respond to a limited number of questions. Cognitive agents can be programmed to learn. So far, they are being deployed primarily as front-end customer-service agents, helping to respond to customer inquiries.

While positioning a cognitive agent in consumer-facing positions potentially reduces the workload of human employees, the real benefit is the scalability and speed with which such agents can be deployed, says Nicholas Moch, head of innovation, strategy, and architecture at SEB. "The business case about efficiency is not the main interest. It's about scalability and the fact that we have customer service [solutions] that we can roll out quickly."

As similar services are developed and released by companies investing in this space, the job impact will be felt across countless industries, mainly thanks to the productivity improvements such services can provide.

Productivity Gains at the Expense of Employment

The potential for productivity gains is almost endless. PwC reports that the use of AI technology (including cognitive agents) will provide massive productivity improvements in the next 15 years. Despite still being early in development, PwC[7] believes "AI could contribute up to $15.7 trillion to the global economy in 2030, more than the current output of China and India combined. Of this, $6.6 trillion is likely to come from increased productivity and $9.1 trillion is likely to come from consumption-side effects." Labor productivity improvements will account for 55 percent of that value, says PwC.

Contrast that with current productivity gains. According to the Bureau of Labor Statistics, between 2011 and 2016, employee productivity in the U.S. grew 0.3 percent per year.

The more startling number, however, occurred back in the year 2000. That was the year the US labor force participation rate peaked at 67.3 percent, as shown in the following graph.

US Labor Force Participation Rate

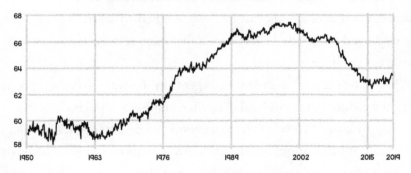

Source: BLS

Since that year, labor force participation has been in a steady decline, despite what you may have heard on the news. What is typically reported is the percentage of people collecting unemployment benefits who have been actively looking for new employment for the past four weeks, also referred to as U3; when that number drops, politicians claim success. But sometimes, because of the definition, people are deleted from the numerator and denominator of the unemployment statistic when they have been unemployed more than 99 weeks. People fall off the unemployment rolls over time, with many unable to find new employment. In other words, they give up looking for work. And those numbers aren't reflected on any of the government's reports. If you are one of those people, it's doubtful you are applauding the politicians who are claiming success. Reductions in unemployment rates do not necessarily mean that there is higher labor-force participation.

The truth is that 67.3 percent of Americans over the age of 16 were working in 2000, and in 2019, that number has fallen to around 63 percent where it has hovered for the last 5 years. As Digital Labor deploys and scales in the market, we will see a drop-in workforce participation as technologies like cognitive agents increasingly assume a larger percentage of tasks now performed by humans.

In addition, when you combine the workforce participation rate with nominal and adjusted median income, you get a much better picture of what's really going on. The fact is, workers are making what they made back in 2000, but fewer people, as a percentage of the total, are making it; the median wage has remained constant, at just under $59,000, between 2000 and 2016. As you can see from the following graph, the top quintile is doing quite well, the middle three quintiles are stagnant, and the bottom quintile is struggling.

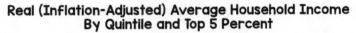

Real (Inflation-Adjusted) Average Household Income By Quintile and Top 5 Percent

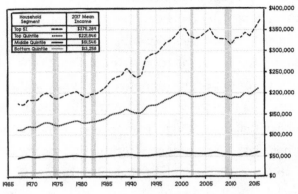

Household Segment		2017 Mean Income
Top 5%	━━━	$375,289
Top Quintile	•••••	$221,846
Middle Quintile	━━	$61,546
Bottom Quintile	━━━	$13,258

Source: US Census Bureau

One of the primary forces of this shift in the market is the deployment of software and software-based platforms that are improving the productivity of the remaining labor force, which then leads to a lower demand for overall labor to perform a process. Today, the more structured a process, the more the process can be automated. As automations become more sophisticated, software will be able to handle less-structured processes and will go well beyond improving productivity to eliminating large groups of knowledge workers.

Jobs that Are Being Phased Out

There are countless examples of fields where automated software programs are replacing human workers. In the accounting, legal, construction, retail, food service, manufacturing, and even agriculture industries, Digital Labor is making its presence known. Automation is affecting industries across the board and around the globe.

Accounting is not typically a field where you picture easily automatable tasks. Yet the rising popularity and consumer use of software programs to crunch numbers has spread to the professional side, where tax-preparation software is now frequently used by CPAs to process financial reports provided by individual and business clients. Much of the data input and simple calculations are now done by tax software, rather than by the accountants themselves. We're nearly to the point where accountants are needed only to check over the calculations and investigate more esoteric tax loopholes.

The ranks of bookkeepers, which are closely related to accountants, will also be thinned through technological change. Demand for bookkeepers is forecast to decline through 2026, according to the Bureau of Labor Statistics[8], with software and cloud computing making it possible for the same amount of work to be done by fewer people. QuickBooks and similar software services can now be relied on to reduce data entry errors by locating and fixing them; these services can also review financial records in search of questionable figures. Tasks formerly done by humans are now done by cognitive agents in a fraction of the time.

The legal sector is also being impacted at a quickening pace. Deloitte Insight[9] predicts that 114,000 jobs in the legal field, or 39 percent of the jobs in that sector, will be eliminated and replaced by software and machines. Most of those positions are administrative, legal secretary roles, which Deloitte suggests will then be replaced with higher-paying, but fewer, positions required to manage all the new technologies.

Manufacturing concerns introduced robot labor decades ago, but having seen the dramatic productivity improvements with increased automation, they are now ramping up their installation. At Foxconn Technology Group (a China-based supplier of Apple and Samsung products), the use of robots enabled the company to cut its workforce from 110,000 to 50,000 human employees.[10]

The company explained that its increasing reliance on robots was a way to enable employees to focus on higher-level, strategic tasks:

"We are applying robotics engineering and other innovative manufacturing technologies to replace repetitive tasks previously done by employees, and through training, also enable our employees to focus on higher value-added elements in the manufacturing process, such as research and development, process control and quality control."

Supporting human work was also the impetus behind the semi-automatic mason (SAM)[11] designed to handle many of the rote movements associated with brick-laying. Working alongside a human mason, a SAM can pick up bricks, apply mortar, and lay the bricks in place while a human mason follows behind to clean up excess mortar. While a human mason can lay approximately 300-500 bricks a day by hand, a SAM can lay 800-1,200 bricks a day. Furthermore, SAM's creator claims a human and SAM, working together, can accomplish the same amount of work as four or more masons.

"SAM's purpose is to leverage human jobs," claims SAM's developer, since it cannot function without having a human first set it up and load it with bricks, but its speed and accuracy is a bit disconcerting for some bricklayers.

Where SAM was designed to supplement human labor, some robots are being designed to replace it, and developers are not shy about stating that. The rising cost of labor, and in some areas the dearth of agricultural workers, has led to efforts to try and automate the process of farming. A farm in the U.K.[12] seems to have done it.

The Hands Free Hectare project was completed in the fall of 2017, with 4-½ tons of barley produced without a single human hand. The soil was prepped, seeds were sown, and plants harvested all remotely, without human involvement.

Likewise, the food-service industry seems to have an interest in replacing at least some of its workers with self-service kiosks and robots. Former McDonald's CEO Ed Rensi[13] explained:

"It's cheaper to buy a $35,000 robotic arm than it is to hire an employee who is inefficient, making $15 an hour bagging French fries."

Rensi's comments are in response to reports out of Wendy's that the company will install 1,000 self-service kiosks in its restaurants by year-end 2017. He confirmed:

"I have said that robots are going to replace people in the service industry going forward," Rensi said. "And a self-service kiosk is nothing more than automation taking over people."

McKinsey estimates that about 51 percent of work processes can be turned over to a machine or robot. Those activities "most susceptible" to automation are "physical ones in highly structured and predictable environments," claims McKinsey, which includes industries mentioned here—food service and hospitality, manufacturing, and retail.

Research firms such as McKinsey Global Institute and many others have predicted that cognitive technologies, such as artificial intelligence, machine learning and automation will eliminate a significant portion of U.S. jobs in the next 5 to 10 years. Depending on what report you read, the number of jobs impacted is as high as 50 percent of the current workforce. The actual number is less important than the issue of whether the impact from these technologies will eliminate the job or transform it. Also, there is the issue of what new jobs get created that compensate for the net losses.

Whatever most reports are saying, I think that number is low, and I would more align to Elon Musk's point of view[14]: "There certainly will be job disruption. Because what's going to happen is robots will be able to do everything better than us ... I mean all of us," said Musk, speaking to the National Governors Association in July 2017.

The UK-based Oxford Martin Program on Technology and Employment[15] estimates that 47 percent of U.S. employees are at risk of being replaced by machines. I suspect that number is getting closer to our future reality, but I would say it's not that employees are being replaced, but, rather, that parts of their jobs will no longer be necessary. There will be consolidation and cuts that then result in wide-scale layoffs and downsizing. McKinsey reports that because most jobs are varied, requiring constant change, adaptation, and a multitude of skills, only a small percentage of existing jobs can be completely replaced by robots; most jobs cannot be fully replaced. I think that estimate is too conservative, given the speed at which cognitive agents are teaching themselves new skills. Yes, they no longer need humans to teach them; they can teach themselves at an alarmingly fast rate. Additionally, we need to think about how business process and workflows will change in reaction to advancing technology. Without changing our processes, the job replacement rate may be somewhat low. However, after redesigning the workflow leveraging the next generation of technology, the job impact could be substantial.

We're at an Inflection Point

Until now, the software that has been developed and has been in use is passive. Passive software is a tool that is used by humans to do something better, such as calculating numbers in TurboTax or processing online-shopping orders based on pre-programmed if/then instructions. Passive software improves overall productivity, by assuming parts of a task formerly performed by humans, such as Amazon's use of robots to pick and pack customer orders. The number of robots in use inside Amazon warehouses has increased by 50 percent in the last year alone, by the way, from 30,000 in 2016 to 45,000 in 2017.[16] But such software is reactive: it needs human input in order to function.

What we are currently witnessing is the tipping point between passive and active software. We are seeing more examples of software that can function without human intervention and that can even teach itself new information and capabilities. Active software can monitor information and take action and make decisions on its own based on environmental cues, rather than direction or prompting from humans.

The Google car, for example, takes action in traffic based on multiple input variables. No driver is needed to watch the highway ahead or the cars around it; the software is constantly monitoring its environment to anticipate the action that may be needed to avoid a collision and to safely get to its destination. While there is still resistance to the idea of driverless cars, we are quickly approaching the point at which human drivers will be less effective in the driver's seat than the car's operating software.

Or consider Google Duplex[17], which was announced in May 2018. Google Duplex is the technology behind Google Assistant, which can interact with others vocally on your behalf. Google Assistant can be set up to sound just like you and to make outbound calls on your behalf. No longer will you need to call to make restaurant reservations, schedule hair appointments, set up meetings, or perform other similar tasks: Google Assistant can do that for you and provide a transcript of the call for reference. Not only does the service free up your time, but it removes more mundane tasks from your to-do list.

The implications for work are staggering, likely starting in call centers. Instead of hiring more workers to place and receive phone calls, companies are now investing in this technology to replace call centers and their workers. Soon the need for physical space and human operators will be nearly non-existent in this industry.

We're currently in the early stages of active software in production environments. As organizations and industries get comfortable with software making decisions, we will see a rapid deployment in the affected industries. That's when we'll see jobs disappear. It's coming sooner than you expect.

Software Can Now Teach Itself

The idea of software or robots being able to self-teach sounds like a science-fiction novel, but it is the new reality. Reports in late 2017 that a software program had bested a world champion Go player sure sounded like fantasy, but it wasn't. Go is an ancient Chinese game with simple rules that are surprisingly complex. Google's DeepMind group decided to try and develop a program that could win at Go, much like computers were developed to win at the game of chess more than 20 years ago. DeepMind developed a program (which it named AlphaGo), which successfully beat world champion Lee Sedol in a series of matches in 2016. What was even more surprising than the win was that "[AlphaGo] played some surprising yet highly effective moves that went against centuries of accumulated wisdom about how the game works," reported an article following the match.[18]

While that win in 2016 was noteworthy, only a year later, DeepMind announced that a new version of the program, AlphaGo Zero, outperformed its predecessor. The level of mastery it took AlphaGo to reach in 2016 required several months and 30 million training games; it took AlphaGo Zero only 3 days and 4.9 million training games to reach that same point. AlphaGo Zero *trained itself* to become the best Go player in the world, with no human intervention or historical data. And where AlphaGo analyzed thousands of previously played games between humans to start to recognize move and patterns, AlphaGo Zero began only with the rules of the game.

The new programs' architecture is also somewhat different. AlphaGo used two neural networks—one to predict the best move and the other to predict the winner of the game based on its moves. During play, the first network would decide on a move while the second network ran a series of quick "what-if" simulations to determine the next best move. In AlphaGo Zero, the two neural networks were combined into one, allowing it to more quickly process the next best move based on predictions of its success. The result? The program learned faster and better, all on its own. The system that no one thought could be beat was beat only 9 months later—and it was 10 times better.

Examples like Alpha Go, Google Duplex, and the semi-automatic mason (SAM) leverage a variety of technologies and architectures. Much of the automation that we hear about is not new per se, but some of the technology deployed in automation solutions is very new and evolving rapidly.

At Rumjog, we developed a framework to help show how these various technologies work together to drive us to the inflection point of change. We call it the Rumjog Automation Maturity Model (RAMM).

The RAMM construct, to be explained in detail in Chapter 3, is designed to help us organize the various technologies and see how they relate to each other, how they complement each other, and how the combination of these technologies is driving businesses to truly transformative operations.

CHAPTER 3:

The Rumjog Automation Maturity Model (RAMM)

"Automation and AI will lift productivity and economic growth, but millions of people worldwide may need to switch occupations or upgrade skills."

- McKinsey Global Institute

CHANGE IS COMING, of that we are sure, but the pace of that technological change varies across industries and processes. There is little consensus regarding the size, scope, and rate of the changes we will soon witness, though we know it's going to be big, causing massive upheaval across the board.

How Driverless Cars Will Change the Landscape—Literally

Take the automotive industry, for example. There have been consistent improvements in safety, fuel-efficiency, and design through the years, but nothing truly revolutionary until after 2010. The development of the electric car and then the driverless car were huge leaps forward in terms of leveraging technology. Once sales and production of the self-driving car reaches a tipping point, there will be major ripple effects across several industries. The pace of change is quickening by the day, but until the late 2010s you might not have noticed it.

Looking back, you may be able to recognize some of the important milestones. The development of the first production vehicle powered by gasoline is generally credited to Karl Benz around 1885. That innovation signaled the future obsolescence of horse-driven carriages and buggy whips. In 1913, the Ford Motor Company rolled out the Model T automobile—the first mass-produced car. It took only about 14 years for more than 15 million Model Ts to come off the assembly line, creating the need for paved roads, traffic signals, gas stations, and garages, among many other things.

While automotive design has slowly evolved, resulting in those massive Cadillacs and Chevy station wagons in the mid-1950s, and then smaller coupes and sedans towards the end of the century as gas prices started to creep up, really, not much has changed. Cars still have basically the same shape. However, there *have* been significant advancements with respect to operation, starting with cruise control in the 1970s. Rather than requiring human intervention to keep a car at a steady pace, you could then lock the accelerator in place and take your foot off the gas, which is a convenient feature to have on long stretches of highway.

The next frontier was passenger safety, which took a big leap forward with mandated use of seat belts in 1996 and standard equipment airbags as of 1998. The introduction of front bumper radar in the early 2000s and rear-view cameras, made standard after 2012, helped reduced pedestrian deaths. Bluetooth technology, to support hands-free cell-phone use, is another recent feature considered standard as of 2010. Even more recent, the addition of radar sensors on the car's exterior makes it possible for cars to avoid accidents when other vehicles come too close. Or adaptive cruise, where radar and cruise control work together to slow a car down or speed it up to avoid colliding with another driver, is an example of more sophisticated technology.

Right now, we're on the cusp of a true driverless car, thanks to the integration and stacking of multiple innovations. Technology integration has advanced to the point that cars can essentially manage the process of moving from point A to point B without human involvement. An autonomous car can sense, thanks to radar, when other vehicles, structures, or living beings are in their way and adjust its path or speed accordingly to stay on the road and travel to its ultimate destinations. Human labor is needed only to provide destination information. The car can make decisions under certain situations, thanks to its advanced software platform. As a result, the car's design is also quickly changing, adding more seating and eliminating the steering wheel, for example.

Although driverless cars are currently being piloted in certain major markets, the day will soon come when they are the standard. Then people will question whether they actually need to own a car. After all, if they can have a car show up at their doorstep when they need it and then transport them where they want to go without their having to concentrate on the task of driving, they can reclaim minutes or hours every day to read or sleep or catch up on work during the drive.

By taking people out of the equation, there will be major changes in the transportation industry. Beyond the primary impact to the numbers of truck drivers and taxi drivers employed, the entire industry can be transformed. Let's look at an example.

Imagine that without the need for drivers, Uber acquires a fleet of driverless vehicles that is 100 times its current size. The company will be able to offer rides reliably and for much lower costs than it does today. This may and will likely call into question the need to own a car at all.A new car can cost $500 to $1,000/month, depending on the type of car and where you live. When you factor in the indirect costs of your time, parking, even having a garage in your home, the costs could well exceed $1,000/month. If your Uber costs in this new model are $500/month compared to $1,000/month, you may think twice about owning a car and simply rent a car on the rare occasion that you want to drive. That is what people in New York City do, and the economics of the driverless can make that a nationwide practice.

If this happens, the secondary and tertiary effects of people no longer owning vehicles far exceeds the impact of job losses from truck drivers and taxi drivers. What happens to gas stations, auto parts industry, car dealers, etc.? What new businesses get created from this new model? Perhaps offer a free Uber ride if you come to our restaurant?

The elimination of human workers from the delivery and operation of a business have a much bigger impact than potential job losses to the economy and society as a whole. It can be transformative.

Human Workers are Becoming Obsolete

Eliminating the need for human involvement in the driving process looks a lot like what happened in the movie-rental business. From around 1992 to 2004, Blockbuster was *the* place to rent movies. You would stop by a store on your way home from work and pick up a recently released movie and some popcorn to snack on. A cashier would check you out and you'd be on your way. The next day, you'd return your videotape—later, your DVD—in the drop box on the store's exterior. Behind the scenes, employees would check the movies back in and place them on store shelves to signal that they were available for rental.

And then Netflix arrived on the scene in the late 1990s, wreaking havoc on Blockbuster's business model. Netflix didn't need physical storefronts or even people to process transactions—rentals were initiated online and CDs were dropped in the mail to arrive at your home within a day or two. Sure, you had to plan ahead, but Netflix's website allowed you to queue up movies to watch whenever they became available (when someone else returned them).

The rental process became even less labor-intensive when Netflix moved to live-streaming of movies. Then customers could watch whatever they wanted with a few clicks on their computer or TV, and even fewer employees were needed. They were slowly cut out of the process altogether.

Something similar is happening at Uber, where drivers there today are contract, not full-time, and used on an as-needed basis. Uber drivers operate their own vehicles and pick-up fares using Uber-developed technology. But as driverless cars are introduced, there will be a declining need for actual drivers. The good news is that as driver jobs fall, the need for engineering and software automation jobs will rise.

What Does "Automated" Really Mean?

Changes that are coming are due to increasingly sophisticated levels of automation. However, there is confusion and disagreement about what, exactly, constitutes automation. The language used to describe automation is imprecise and frequently at odds.

In fact, "automation" can refer to anything from mechanization to artificial intelligence, which is why when several companies claim to have automated their processes, it's important to drill down to discover what they mean by "automated." Many people seem to think that automation is an either/or paradigm, rather than a spectrum of complexity—that it is a single-state condition.

It's not.

That becomes a problem when we try to assess and accurately communicate where organizations are in terms of their use of advanced computing power.

Companies may think they are highly automated when their comparative level of automation is rudimentary at best. In fact, there are different levels of complexity and maturity when it comes to automation. (We at Rumjog have identified six.)

For example, when some companies hear the word automation, employees may nod their heads in unison that their process is entirely automated. What they're referring to is the mechanization of some or all of their production process—i.e., task automation. That is not the only definition of the word, however, and other companies use the term automation to mean the development and testing of advanced artificial intelligence bots. The two uses of the term automation are correct but refer to very different applications.

To provide clarity, Rumjog developed a model that presents levels of advancement with respect to automation on a six-point scale from 0 to 5, or labor-based to highly evolved. The goal of the Rumjog Automation Maturity Model (RAMM) is to clear up confusion regarding how advanced certain organizations are and to foster consensus on what the different levels of automation maturity are.

Much like earthquakes, each successive level within the model has an even greater impact on society than prior levels—capabilities are added at each higher level—with resulting improvements in cost-effectiveness, quality, and speed. Those are the advantages of advances in automation at every level.

Rumjog Automation Maturity Model

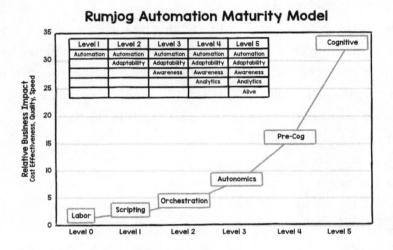

Level 1	Level 2	Level 3	Level 4	Level 5
Automation	Automation	Automation	Automation	Automation
	Adaptability	Adaptability	Adaptability	Adaptability
		Awareness	Awareness	Awareness
			Analytics	Analytics
				Alive

Rumjog Automation Maturity Model: Levels 0-5

0 = Manual labor. No automation.

1 = Scripts. Simple, stand-alone tasks completed by software.

2 = Orchestration. A series of tasks completed by software.

3 = Autonomics. Software programs are aware of their environment and make decisions accordingly, without human involvement.

4 = Pre-cognitive. Software can anticipate future events on its own.

5 = Cognitive. Software becomes alive.

Level 0: Manual Labor

Companies not yet using automation are at a pre-automation stage, where manual labor is unaided by advanced technology. This is RAMM level 0. At this stage, for example:

- workers harvest fruits and vegetables from fields by hand,
- maid services clean homes top-to-bottom under their own power, and
- assembly workers put together component pieces of products by hand.

There are few efficiencies at this stage, or efficiency depends entirely on the skill and speed of the human worker. There is no automation.

Level 1: Scripts

At level 1, we see task automation using simple scripts—the first step in automated processes. Scripts are simple programs—software code—that can automatically run a series of steps to complete a task. Scripts are considered a technology building block and work best when the tasks being scripted follow standard, repeatable if/then steps. Here are a few examples of simple task automation:

- motion sensor lights that come on when someone enters a room,
- a Roomba vacuum cleaner that moves around a room until it hits an obstacle, or
- even mathematical commands within an Excel spreadsheet.

These scripts increase efficiency and productivity, especially in situations with repetitive tasks, by replacing the need for human intervention. A coffee maker that can be set to turn on at 6:00 am is another example, as is a car's basic cruise-control function. Drivers can turn on cruise control and relinquish the task of staying at a standard speed to the car's internal programming.

At this level there is only basic automation.

Level 2: Orchestration

The next level up the automation scale is orchestration, when scripts are stitched together to complete a more complex workflow or process. Orchestration in new cars today exists with adaptive cruise control. Two technologies: front bumper radar and basic cruise control work together the deliver adaptive cruise. Adaptive cruise will maintain speed on the highway, but if traffic ahead slows down, your car will automatically slow down and speed back to desired speed when the traffic ahead clears. This is Level 2 orchestration.

Another example of orchestration can be found, not surprisingly, in music. In classical music, think of the individual instruments—the violins, cellos, and trumpets—as the scripts at Level 1. In Level 2, the conductor is responsible for guiding all the individual musicians to play a music arrangement—separate but together to play something like a symphony.

In Level 2, we combine two concepts: automation and adaptability. It is the combination of technologies that have these two attributes that constitute Level 2 orchestration.

Beyond the car and music examples, think of Level 1 and 2 as technology that can complete individual or a series of processes that were once triggered by humans. The more the software does (vs. human), the higher the efficiency gains made at each successive level as humans become less essential to the completion of the task. For example, instead of manually copying and pasting data into a spreadsheet, at level 1 a bot can be pre-programmed to automatically do the copying and pasting based on set rules. At level 2, bots can complete larger and more complex tasks as multiple process bots are linked.

Level 3: Autonomics

Level 3 is a game changer—the point at which control flips from humans to technology; humans no longer drive the process. In Level 3, the technology is replacing the "worker" in the process.

Up to this point in Levels 1 and 2, the technology is a tool to be used to make the people who are performing the work more productive. In that sense the technology is passive, like a tool that has to be used by a person. If the person doesn't know how to use the tool, the tool is useless. Think of some of the features in software that just sit there because you do not know how to use them.

In Level 3—the technology pivots to an active role and operates itself without the need for a human operator. At this level, the automated system has the ability to understand what's happening in the environment and adjust the related processes in response. It can orchestrate features and functions without human interaction or intervention. The technologies can talk to one another allowing for an autonomous solution. This level is autonomics.

In our car example, the Google Car is at Level 3. Where levels 1 and 2 made the human driver increasingly efficient, by Level 3, the driver has been replaced; there is no need for human participation. What is revolutionary about the Google Car is its ability to process inputs about its environment and make decisions accordingly—on its own. So, for example, if the car needed to make a left-hand turn, it would take into account the angle of the turn, the car's turning radius, the amount of traffic, traffic signals, and navigate the turn based on all of those data points.

In our music example, Level 3 would be a jazz riff, where all of the players in the band adapt and respond to what the other musicians are playing. Or in the stock market, an autonomic system can trade in real-time on its own, given basic parameters you set. Unlike the Level 2 tax platform, which serves up the same questions for you to answer, at Level 3, only relevant questions are presented based on previous responses.

With Level 3, we add technology awareness on top of the automation and adaptability present in the first two levels.

Level 4: Pre-Cognitive

At the pre-cognitive level, analytics are added to the mix, enabling the system to begin to anticipate the future based on its analysis of past events. Pre-cognitive systems can "see things" before they happen, or before problems arise. While humans can do this in simple environments, pre-cognitive platforms can evaluate thousands of variables in real time to look for system anomalies and then respond accordingly.

In the automotive market, a pre-cognitive car is driverless—it can monitor the roadway, other cars nearby, traffic signals, road conditions, and navigational maps to decide the best route to take, at what speed, modifying its course as needed to avoid collisions.

Pre-cognitive cars can also be organized to respond to anticipated demand from humans in need of transportation. At Level 4, a fleet of cars can be dispatched ahead of time based on social media posts about human plans. Taking into account, for example, that a major concert is letting out at 11:00 pm downtown, driverless cars could move into that area to meet expected demand. Or by monitoring social media posts that include a couple's plans to leave a party, such as, "Heading out after a great night at the medical society gala," cars can be sent to where the party is being held in advance of any formal request for pick-up.

In stock trading, rather than setting up rules for trades, the pre-cognitive system trades for you, by leveraging market data and analytics and trading algorithms. Pre-cognitive, in a sense, sees the future and acts on it. In finance, that is trading ahead of the market; in driving, it's avoiding future traffic jams based on future traffic indicators or inputs of potential congestion. In music, pre-cognitive may connote adjusting the style or genre of music to what is happening in an environment/setting, such as slowing down the tempo after midnight; a type of contextual music.

Level 5: Cognitive

Once we reach the cognitive level, at Level 5, the computer system itself understands what it is doing. In many ways, it behaves and acts like a human being, making strategic decisions based on advanced analyses of unstructured data. It is what we would consider "alive."

At this stage, the system comprehends what is happening and can participate in or support human decision-making. So instead of improving efficiency by sending cars to a busy area of town (such as would happen at level 4), at level 5, the system might prompt the human user to head home from the party in order to be well-rested for work tomorrow or because of an impending shift of cars to another part of town.

The output of such a cognitive system may be prescriptive, suggestive, informing, or unexpected, much like what humans choose to share. Computers at this stage are in a prescient state, interacting with humans the way humans interact with each other.

Very few technologies are Level 5 at this point, but we're getting close quickly.

To summarize the maturity model using our car example, the RAMM would look like this:

Level	Level Description	Level Attributes	Car example
0	Manual labor		
I	Scripts	Automation	Cruise Control
2	Orchestration	Adaptability	Adaptive Cruise
3	Autonomics	Awareness	Google Car (Autonomous Driving/Self-Driving)
4	Pre-cognitive	Analytics	Predictive Routing
5	Cognitive	Alive	Prescriptive Routing

Barclay's Leverages Automation for Higher Profit

Although there are no examples yet of companies that have reached level 5, there are many that are moving in that direction. Take Barclay's Bank's mortgage processing unit, for example.

Paperwork and financial analyses that the bank formerly needed weeks to process can now be completed in days or hours by automated systems. By effectively removing humans from the process, data provided by home buyers can be analyzed in seconds and a decision made in a fraction of the time it used to take.

As a result, the cost of mortgage processing has declined toward zero due to automation and profitability has risen, in part due to Barclay's ability to charge a ¼-point premium for faster mortgage processing. Customers are willing to pay a little more to be able to close on their dream home in less time, while the use of technology keeps Barclay's costs extremely low. That ¼-point charge is all profit, essentially.

We're also seeing more automation in medicine, with anesthesiologists increasingly replaced by machines that can adjust the delivery of anesthesia based on real-time data from the patient's body. Or systems that can review x-rays and identify anomalies for a doctor to explore further.

Polar Shift

We're currently witnessing a polar shift in the relationship between humans and technology at work. Instead of computers supporting humans, making their work easier and faster, the dynamic is flipping—the poles are reversing—and humans will soon work in a subservient role to technology. Technology will become the driver.

Sound crazy? We're nearly there now.

Pole realignment is underway today, where we sit at the autonomic level—level 3. Level 3 is the inflection point. That is the point at which the business model changes, from people running businesses that are supported by technology to technology leading businesses that are supported by people.

Uber is a great example of this. While you might think of Uber as a transportation company, it is actually a technology platform. The software system that is the backbone of the platform doesn't require people to run it. Human involvement in the process includes those driving the cars that take people from place to place; however, that won't be for much longer.

With driverless cars currently being piloted in Pittsburgh[19] and Phoenix, and Uber stating an intention to buy every driverless car that comes off the assembly line, in a few short years it's very possible that humans won't even be needed as drivers.

What's interesting about this shift in dynamic is Uber's market capitalization—what it's worth. As of mid-2018, it has 12,000 employees[20] and a market cap of $72 billion.[21] That means that the average market cap per employee is $6 million.

Compare that with Ford Motor Company, one of the largest car companies in the world. It is a labor-intensive company with about 200,000 employee and a market cap of $37 billion, which is about $185,000 of market cap per employee. This a fraction of the market cap per employee that Uber generates.

Facebook's market cap is about $14 million per employee. Compare to old media company like Gannett at a market cap of $70,000 per employee. The business model has already pivoted, believe it or not.

But Uber and Facebook are not outliers. Their new digital businesses have similar profiles to their analog counterparts. The companies simply rely less on people to generate value. There is even the concept of zero employees in constructs call DACs—distributed autonomous corporations. Take a look at Deepart.io, which is a digitally autonomous company that creates, sells, and ships computer-generated artwork. That is, there are no employees—it is run entirely by technology. Yes, five researchers from Germany, Switzerland, and Belgium wrote the code to establish the business, but now orders are taken electronically, and the purchased art is generated by technology.

It's actually quite an innovative process. Customers upload their own photo and then choose an artistic style they prefer and the Deepart server then applies the artistic style to the photo, creating an entirely new piece of art based on those two factors. The piece is then printed as a poster or art piece and shipped out.

Short of DACs are end-to-end business processes that operate without the need for humans. In legacy corporations, end-to-end process automation is the Holy Grail in automation transformation. It is very hard to pivot from the human-based process to one that is fully automated. It is much easier to design the automated process from scratch.

Science Fiction Is Becoming Reality

What seemed far-fetched just months ago is already becoming reality in this new age of Digital Labor. The Rumjog Automation Maturity Model offers a framework for understanding the different types of automation and the associated impacts on business environments like yours. It provides a language we can use to better describe the levels of automation organizations are relying on as we shift from a human workforce to Digital Labor.

At levels 4 and 5, entirely new business models will emerge, based in large part on the data being generated. We're already seeing companies like Google and Facebook data mining for information about consumers, in search of products and services they are likely to be interested in buying, based on their search history. What's beyond that, we expect, is the rise of an experience economy, where experiences, such as travel and education, become more important than acquiring more stuff as we move into level 3 and beyond.

But we are not fortune tellers. We don't know everything. And we're not sure that anyone can know everything in this fast-changing market. But it helps to have a common language with which to discuss what's happening.

PART II:

Business Implications:
What are the Opportunities?

CHAPTER 4:

The Workforce Impact

"The role of humans as the most important factor of production is bound to diminish in the same way that the role of horses in agricultural production was first diminished and then eliminated by the introduction of tractors."

- Nobel Prize-winning economist Wassily Leontief in 1983 as quoted in *The Second Machine Age*

WHEN WE TALK ABOUT WORKFORCE IMPACT, the extent to which change will be felt is going to vary by marketplace and industry. While macroeconomics is one indicator of what's going on, it doesn't tell you the underlying factors that are causing large-scale change.

The technology we've discussed in the first few chapters is an abstraction. People want to understand how this technological shift will impact them. Using an average metric to describe the coming changes—such as average salary, average workforce reduction, or average work week—can distort reality. That's because the direct impact on an individual worker can be catastrophic. We need to understand all the workforce impacts that might affect you and your career before we discuss the pace of change.

Right now, at least, workers can and do perform many tasks as part of their broad job responsibilities. For example, a marketing manager may manage budgets, hire ad agencies, oversee the conceptualization of marketing messages for various target audiences, research potential social media tools, on top of many other responsibilities. In contrast, automation has narrow expertise. Automation might schedule social media posts, for example, or track ad spending. Most automation technologies are created to perform one function or a series of functions, but the technology today generally doesn't yet have the flexibility to be cross-trained as humans can be. Their functionality is tightly focused. However, that is quickly changing. Even tasks we once believed were untouchable, or required human involvement because they require judgment and creativity, are now in jeopardy of becoming automated.

Keeping up not only means jobs are at risk, but entire companies are close to being wiped out and made obsolete, because many do not have the agility to swiftly adjust and embrace disruption quickly enough.

The pace of change in the market now exceeds our ability to keep up with it. That goes for just about anything having to do with technology and especially for knowledge work automation.

Most companies today are smack dab in the middle of the Automation Maturity Model (RAMM), at level 2 or 3. They are at or nearing automation's inflection point, where, instead of using technology to make human workers more efficient and productive, newly developed computing programs and equipment are leading the way. Workers are now managed by software platforms instead of the reverse. It is the tipping point for knowledge work, where automation is increasingly replacing or eliminating tasks that we once thought only humans could complete.

For years we have heard that thanks to technological advancements, we will see productivity increases. And we have. But there will also come a time when we pivot and human workers are needed much less.

Workers today are able to accomplish so much more on a typical day thanks to new developments in software. We measure that productivity improvement by dividing production output by labor. The only problem is that, thanks to those same technological advances, output is no longer a function of labor. In fact, the two are becoming decoupled. Technology is now eliminating or absorbing tasks that were once productivity factors.

In the book *The Second Machine Age*, MIT economists Erik Brrynjolfs-son and Andrew McAfee introduce the concept of the Great Decoupling. The Great Decoupling, according to their theory, suggests that things that formerly tracked together, meaning in parallel, are decoupling as we introduce technology in the delivery of goods and services. In this case, we're talking about labor productivity, real gross domestic product (GDP) per capita (meaning the average economic output per person), private employment, and median family income, which are no longer moving in parallel.

At Rumjog, we would further argue that this decoupling will accelerate on a non-linear basis, as advanced technologies progress in their capabilities and deployment.

When Workers Began Falling Behind

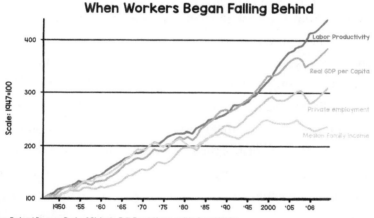

Source : Federal Reserve Bank of St. Louis; Erik Brynjolfsson and Andrew McAfee
From   : "The Great Decoupling," June 2015

"In recent years, technologies like payroll processing software, factory automation, computer-controlled machines, automated inventory control, and word processing have been deployed for routine work, *substituting* for workers in clerical tasks, on the factory floor, and doing rote information processing," point out Brynjolfsson and McAfee.

But even as jobs are increasingly being replaced by technology, there are still many pockets of tasks that only humans can perform. Those pockets exist at the edge of transformation's capabilities. We need people at this edge to expand automation capabilities—the people with edge expertise are becoming an expert class and their knowledge is highly sought after. As Brynjolfsson and McAfee observe, "people with the right engineering, creative, or design skills" can augment those skills through technologies like "big data and analytics, high-speed communications, and rapid prototyping."

The result? "The net effect has been to decrease demand for less-skilled labor while increasing the demand for skilled labor," say the authors. The more you can adapt your skills and ability to manage the edge of technology transformation, the more secure your job is.

How do we identify work at the edge versus more routine work? Routine and structured work performed by humans is where we will see the short-term transformations of technology. At the edge of transformation, it is neither routine nor structured, so we need people, a new expert class, with knowledge of processes and workflows to push the boundaries of what can be automated.

To illustrate this point, let's consider the difference between a cook and a chef. A cook follows strict instructions on a recipe, creating meals per the required ingredients, preparation techniques, and cook time. A chef can cook, but, in addition, has the ability to create and adapt to dynamic environmental conditions, such as making veal parmesan without any cheese or developing entirely new dishes for patrons on demand. We see this skill demonstrated on the many cooking shows on cable TV, where trained chefs compete to produce appealing dishes with a set of odd ingredients or atypical conditions. So, while a cook performs the task of routinely combining ingredients according to a set recipe, a chef creates new combinations and dishes, with few restrictions beyond the ingredients available at the moment.

Another way to think about it is this: routine work performed by humans can be classified as human middleware, much like software of the same name. Think of human middleware as work performed by people who are following a set of rules and procedures under structured conditions. It is this human middleware that is highly prone to automation in this early phase of transformation. Which means that we will end up needing far fewer cooks, since software can do that work, and more chefs.

More on The Great Decoupling

As mentioned in Chapter 2, take a look at US labor force participation, which rose steadily from 1972 to 2000 along with average wages. As more employees entered the workforce, wages continued to rise in concert. In the year 2000, workforce participation was highly correlated with other economic indicators, but very quickly the two variables became uncorrelated. It was in 2000 that workforce participation peaked in the US at 67.3 percent—from then on, that percentage has steadily declined. By late 2013, it crossed below 63 percent and has remained roughly flat for the last 5+ years. When automation expands beyond the current edge, we expect to see a significant drop in workforce participation in the future.

But there's something else problematic about this labor force participation data. Namely, that it's a binary measure—you're either working or you're not. Yet participation is not a binary measure. In order to fully appreciate the workforce participation, you need to look at the other measures and factors to get the whole picture.

Let's say you have an $80,000-a-year job working for a bank and you get laid off. You can't find another job in banking at that salary level, so you take a $30,000-a-year job at a retail store to pay your bills. Yes, you're employed full-time, but you're not employed to your full capacity. You may put in 40 hours, but the tasks you're assigned are not as challenging as in your last job. But on the labor force participation chart, you're recorded in the win column—you're working, you're participating. That's the problem with relying solely on the labor participation statistic to gauge the health of the employment markets.

Which leads me to wonder what percentage of the roughly 63 percent who are in the labor force are employed to their full capacity. Are they working in a position that is aligned with their education and training? Or are they stringing together three part-time jobs to be able to make ends meet?

As workforce participation has been on a steady decline since 2000, the spread between the top and the bottom of the labor pool, from a compensation perspective, has widened dramatically. At the top are the multimillionaires and billionaires—the notorious 1 percent—where it is not uncommon to experience wage increases of 20 percent or more per year. Yet the bottom half of the labor pool is not experiencing anything close to 20 percent labor increases per year.

While the average income of the bottom three quintiles dropped (meaning those workers were making even less than they had been), at the top, earners were raking in the dough, making much more than they ever had. The top earners offset the drop in the earning power in the bottom quintiles, which kept the average income of $59,000 in 2000 the same as in 2017. Given inflation, that means the standard of living for most workers declined.

The root cause? The relative value of the labor being contributed to the economy is shifting depending on the type of job. Specifically, some types of labor are increasing in value and other types of labor are shrinking in value. Nursing, engineering, data scientists, lab technicians, or, more broadly, experts at the edge of labor automation, are seeing healthy wage increases. Cashiers, call center operators, drivers, or, more broadly, jobs that are on the current front lines of automation, are seeing wage pressures because too many people are chasing the same jobs.

While people will retrain and shift their skill sets, the shift in supply is moving at a glacial pace. This mismatch creates an oversupply in lower-skilled jobs and undersupply in most highly skilled jobs. Think of it this way: the emerging need for labor in the economy is strongest in the expert or skilled class of labor, but there are not enough skilled people to fill these jobs and there are too many people in job classes that are experiencing a decline in demand. Herein lies the key reason for the difference in labor compensation between the top and bottom of the labor markets.

As an example, there is an explosion in demand for cybersecurity professionals, but the supply is scarce. Consequently, we're see skyrocketing wages in this space. In contrast, in low-skilled jobs like retail, we see stagnant wages because the demand for these jobs is waning, and the supply of labor is abundant.

Labor pools need to shift from low-skilled areas to more niche experts areas, but this requires time. Retraining or reskilling is not something that can be accomplished overnight. Further, the higher-value jobs often require advanced education and higher-than-normal IQs to be valuable. While many workers can be retrained to become data scientists or cybersecurity analysts, it is worth pointing out that half the population has an IQ of 100 or less. This may sound harsh, but if you lack the intellectual capacity to do more advanced work, no amount of retraining or reskilling will compensate. It's quite likely that people without the right mix of aptitude and attitude will be unable to be trained to the higher-skilled labor classes, no matter how much time you give them.

As technology progresses and performs more and more of the work, the remaining labor or residual labor to be accomplished becomes more complex. It is this complexity that is defining tomorrow's experts and makes these experts' skills increasingly scarce. Said another way, the available work or work remaining in the wake of automation will require a high level of expertise that will become harder and harder to come by. Which is why the wages of experts and those managing the edge of transformation are increasing more rapidly compared to the other groups.

The progression of what's coming seems obvious to us and there is an increasing awareness (albeit slowly) that automation and advanced technologies are going to impact the job markets. However, because these predictions have been made for years, if not decades, we have become desensitized to the commentary, bordering on skeptical.

We've watched science fiction movies like *Ex Machina, Her*, and *I, Robot* that have hinted at what's to come. Many futurists have warned of the coming obsolescence of humans, which seems far-fetched to many, but few futurists have shown the full impact of technology on our economy and, specifically, on the ability to earn a living. The fact is that most people may not be able to afford the modern conveniences presented in their future view. The Android robot that cooks, cleans, and drives your kid to school is a great vision, but who can afford it and how much does it cost? No one has that answer yet.

It's easy to be overwhelmed by these questions, and the common reaction is to put your head down and focus on your job, preferring not to consider an uncertain future that may be coming sooner than we think. It's what a lot of people are doing right now.

The problem with that approach is that pretending change isn't coming leaves workers unprepared. Those who recognize the need to adapt to changing market conditions and take steps to acquire the skill sets to work with advanced technology will move into higher-knowledge work—the top quintiles dominated by expert labor. And those who opt to ignore the warnings will likely be looking for other work—work that requires fewer skills and pays a lower salary.

Digital Innovations

It is important to note that the digital technologies that are disrupting existing jobs are also creating a whole new set of jobs. The issue is that they aren't creating the same number of jobs at the same pace, scale, and location. For example, let's say that 100 jobs are eliminated through a technology deployment and 20 new jobs are created. Sometimes, the 20 new jobs come from the 100 jobs that are impacted, but more often they do not. So, the challenge we now have is finding employment for the hundreds of jobs that are impacted and sourcing the 20 new jobs that are created, which usually have a very different skill set.

Let's look at a specific example of accounting and financial reporting:

- Today we have finance professionals working to close the books each month (consolidations, reconciliations, accruals, posting data, report generation, etc.).

- When software bots are deployed to perform these activities, we need fewer financial staff plus some software engineering staff to maintain the operation.

- The number of jobs eliminated typically will exceed the number of jobs created.
- The jobs created bear little resemblance to the jobs eliminated.
- The work that is replaced with software will rarely encompass 100 percent of a person's responsibilities in a 40-hour work week, and there will always be some residual labor that must be performed by financial professionals.

This situation creates five new challenges:

1. Organizing the residual labor into structured full-time jobs. Residual labor is often expert in nature and episodic, meaning that the expertise is required at non-regular intervals that may be hard to anticipate and plan for.
2. Restacking the aggregate residual labor into a new organizational structure.
3. Finding gainful employment for displaced financial professionals.
4. Acquiring new software engineers to support the operation. In many cases, the software engineers are in short supply.
5. Delaying with a moving target. None of this is static—the changes to the environment are highly dynamic and accelerating, requiring solving the above four challenges continuously.

An Emerging Conflict of Interest: Labor vs. Technology

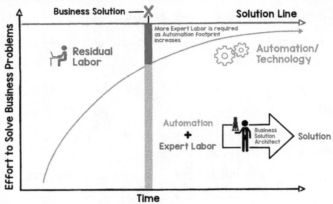

As seen in the above illustration, over time, as automation and technology complete more and more of the workflow, the residual labor that is left shrinks commensurately. However, as it shrinks, what is left is typically the exception handling and expert work that the technology cannot resolve within the system. Managing, staffing, and procuring the expert labor will become increasingly difficult, requiring reimagined business models with respect to employing experts for a given process.

A source of new jobs is going to emerge from the same digital innovation that's disrupting the job markets. With respect to innovation, the key advantage that digital technology has over traditional analog technology is its ability to scale and deploy at machine speed. For example, consider car design. Humans using the analog approach require take months to conceive of a new design, draw it, engineer it, prototype it, and test it out. In contrast, digital technology can be programmed to complete the task in a fraction of the time. Automated software can consider a new car design from every possible angle and then map it out, weigh various frame advantages and disadvantages and appropriate engine sizes, design several prototypes, and digitally test them in a matter of hours, coming up with an innovative style that would never have been considered in an analog environment.

Where analog decision-making is very systematic, methodical, and often bureaucratic, digital decision-making can happen at machine speed, with alternatives being tested simultaneously. Digital systems can consider multiple options and approaches that humans likely would never have thought of—remember the results of the AlphaGo match mentioned in an earlier chapter, where the software algorithm came up with winning strategies no one had ever considered or seen before?

Additionally, digital software systems also have a near-zero incremental cost. It costs virtually nothing to run a software-based automation program once the platform is installed. Zero marginal cost never applies in a system that requires physical goods or labor to complete.

These digital capabilities are now being put to use where analog processes currently exist. In the pharmaceutical industry, for example, new drugs have historically been required to undergo a series of tests to ensure that there are few adverse effects in humans. It typically takes many years to develop a drug and have it survive and succeed after multiple rounds of clinical trials. That's the analog model.

In the digital realm, pharmaceutical companies are now leveraging computing power to digitally represent, at the molecular level, what a particular drug looks like and how it will behave within the human body. Soon it will be possible to run a series of tests that formerly took years and cost hundreds of millions of dollars to assess a new drug's safety and efficacy in a fraction of that time and at a fraction of that cost. Digital technology is changing how pharmaceutical manufacturers are undertaking testing and development and potentially reducing the final cost of that drug to the consumer (we can hope).

Once developed, digital innovations can also be scaled at warp speed. Unlike the analog world, where products need to be physically designed and built and tested at great expense, digital software systems can conceive of solutions, update them, test them, and scale them in a fraction of the time that the analog development and testing process takes.

Because, on a marginal basis, it costs next to nothing, a digital entity like software-based automation can be used in business to generate ideas for new combinations of things. Called recombinant innovation, this is the process of linking two previously unrelated things to create a newer, better product.

An analog example of this process, which happened organically rather than sparked by digital innovation, is actor George Clooney's liquor brand, Casamigos Tequila. When you think of George Clooney, you think of movies and performance, not booze. And yet his brand is currently worth more than $1 billion, or at least that's what Diageo paid for it in 2017.

Clooney's idea for the line emerged after a steady diet of tequila in Mexico, during the months-long process of building a home there next door to his restaurateur friend Rande Gerber. They sampled many bottles and decided they could do better—a smooth tequila that could be enjoyed on the rocks or mixed and, most important, that wouldn't cause a hangover.

Working with a local distiller in Jalisco, Mexico, the pair made batches for themselves. But along the way, thanks to plenty of drinking and sharing bottles with friends, they exceeded the 1,000-bottle maximum the distiller was permitted to produce without a license. So, they brought in a friend, Michael Meldman, and began marketing it. To say it exceeded their expectations would be a huge understatement.

Success stories like these, of businesses and individuals stumbling onto a major business opportunity in the analog world, are rare. But in the digital world, such new opportunities are common events.

That's because a machine can digest, distill, and create whole new permutations never-before considered. That goes for products, services, applications, process improvements—virtually anything you can think of. Digital systems can do it faster and better.

The Rise of Workforce Syndication

Solving the residual labor problem is a challenge that will require new business models and approaches to how companies acquire and manage labor. Rather than the term "labor," think of the term "talent" to better describe the challenge. Finding an expert in the form of a full-time employee is becoming impractical across many dimensions. The first challenge is that you may require multiple levels of expertise that a single individual rarely possesses. Second, the episodic nature of the work performed by expert talent doesn't lend itself well to filling a 40-hour work week. What would be ideal for the new business model is to buy expertise/talent or residual labor in an on-demand, outcome-based format instead of being tied to effort and employment, as it historically has been.

Perhaps it's not surprising then that we're seeing a huge rise in expert freelancing and the gig economy, for certain types of work. Freelancers are, in a way, working for the technology. The model has flipped. Where human resource management departments used to manage personnel—acquiring the skills and talent needed for the organization to function—in the future, workforce syndication will become the norm. In a syndicate, software systems manage workers, who are assigned tasks based on skill, availability, or cost.

Uber is a familiar contemporary example. The software platform that connects available drivers and clients manages the workflow. Human drivers are really just the spokes in the wheel; the software is the cog, the manager.

Then there's Topcoder, which is a workforce syndicate with 1+ million designers, developers, and data scientists; of those, about 300,000 are active users or workers. On Topcoder, a client posts a project that needs to be completed and a budget for the work. The Topcoder platform then breaks down the workflow into modules and posts them on the platform where programmers can compete for the work. Each year, more than 7,000 projects are completed through Topcoder, and that number is steadily rising.

The notion of a traditional job is being destroyed through these new platforms, which slice and dice tasks and assign them to the best available worker. What's happening on Topcoder is a harbinger of what's to come in the general labor pool.

On Topcoder, the top 20 percent of workers make more essentially freelancing through Topcoder than they did in their last full-time jobs as employees. The best, most highly skilled earn the most. And the bottom 80 percent are left to squabble over the less-desirable projects, where the pay is lower or the work not as exciting. This reality is a mirror for what's starting to play out in America's largest companies. The employees who have skills that will support the labor shift we are witnessing will earn more—they'll be in the top quintile earning-wise. And those employees who aren't keeping up, either because they're not trying or they're not aware of the need to amp up their skills, will be underutilized going forward.

What's interesting about Topcoder, though, is that there is a clear hierarchy of workers and projects. The best-paid workers are clear about their skills, what they're good at, and they stay in that swim lane, making the best use of their skills there. They don't bid on jobs that are beyond their skill set because they know they can't be competitive; they know they would lose out to more advanced coders. So they specialize in the lower-level jobs, where their skills are superior and they do quite well as a result. As of late 2018, a majority of companies are a 2 or 3 on the Rumjog Automation Maturity Model (RAMM), indicating they are at or beyond the inflection point where instead of leveraging technology for productivity improvements, workers are now frequently being leveraged by technology a la Uber and Topcoder.

Digital systems are able to adapt and change, undirected, at a pace that exceeds our ability to learn. While previous major technological shifts eventually plateaued, allowing humans to catch up, this time there is no catching up. Now that technology can function independent of human input, there's no stopping it. Despite the fact that workers today seem unconcerned about the swift pace at which software can now complete much of their jobs, we will soon reach a point at which technology can do nearly everything a human can at work, largely due to digital innovations requiring very low financial investment in comparison to the analog innovation process, which requires costly physical prototyping and testing.

CHAPTER 5:

People – Managing Labor and Re-training the Workforce

"The classic model of education—a burst at the start and top-ups through company training—is breaking down. One reason is the need for new, and constantly updated, skills. Manufacturing increasingly calls for brain work rather than metal-bashing."

- The Economist, January 14, 2017

THE TECHNOLOGICAL ADVANCEMENTS we have witnessed for the past 200 years have dramatically and steadily improved labor productivity, seemingly proving the Luddite fallacy, which states that technology doesn't eliminate jobs, it only changes the composition of jobs available. Thanks to automation and technological enhancements, workers have been capable of an ever-increasing amount of productivity. Year-over-year productivity improvements were the norm during the Industrial Age.

However, in 1930, economist John Maynard Keynes warned that eventually the Luddite fallacy would no longer hold true. Productivity improvements could not continue ad infinitum without some kind of backlash, he predicted in his paper, "Economic Possibilities for our Grandchildren," published in 1930:

> "We are being afflicted with a new disease ... namely, technological unemployment. This means unemployment due to our discovery of means of economising the use of labour outrunning the pace at which we can find new uses for labour."

Turns out he was right, giving way to what we call the Luddite Fallacy Fallacy, which is the point at which technological advances pivoted from becoming job creators to job destroyers. That point arrived in the U.S. in 2000, according to the Bureau of Labor Statistics, when workforce participation began its decline after centuries of increases. Productivity improvements due to technology had reached their tipping point; from that point on, technology has been driving broad economic expansion, but without an equally broad labor participation in all segments and levels of employment. This decoupling of job growth with economic growth has led to increasing wealth concentration for the top 10%-20%.

Do You Need a College Education?

To become employable today, students continue to spend hundreds of thousands of dollars on a college degree; a moderate budget for an in-state university for 2017-2018 was $25,290 and a moderate budget for a private college was $50,900—per year for four years, according to Collegedata. The graph below further details the inflation adjusted percentage change in university tuition throughout the years as well the widening disparity between tuitions and starting salaries. While a college education was once considered a requirement for a well-paying white-collar job, its value is now suspect. Students defer earning a paycheck for four years or more to obtain a degree that, today, may or may not prepare them for the work world. And yet nearly 70 percent of US high school graduates routinely enroll in undergraduate programs at colleges and universities each year, according to the Bureau of Labor Statistics. Yet that number appears to be on the decline: in 2016, 71.9 percent of graduates went on to college.

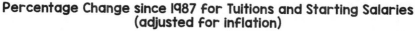

Percentage Change since 1987 for Tuitions and Starting Salaries (adjusted for inflation)

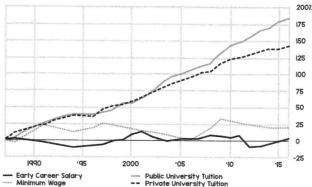

Source: National Center for Education Statistics; National Association of Colleges and Employers; U.S. Department of Labor

Whether a college degree is worth the cost and time often depends on what the student studies. Majoring in Elizabethan poetry, for example, may not yield the payoff at graduation to justify the expense. Sure, studying anything in depth has the power to broaden a student's mind, but more esoteric humanities majors are unlikely to have much practical application in a world where computers are increasingly managing many aspects of our lives.

A 2018 study of the best-paying college degrees by Glassdoor listed science, technology, engineering, and math (STEM) majors at the top, with computer programming, information technology, and engineering often offering average salaries of $65,000 or more within the first five years out of college, where such skills are hot commodities in the corporate world. At the other end of the spectrum, where starting salaries are closer to $40,000, are positions in anthropology, psychology, and biology, possibly because the majority of potential employers are in academia.

That's not to say that obtaining more education is worthless. But students today should think more strategically about the types of job they aspire to hold after graduation. Rather than attending college on the presumption that any college degree will qualify them for a higher-paying position at graduation, students need to weigh the time and cost of such an investment against the potential outcome after four years of study.

Certificate Programs Gaining Momentum

Increasingly, targeted shorter-term certificate programs are becoming more valuable than some traditional four-year degrees. One *U.S. News & World Report* article went so far as to state that: "In some professions, a certificate from a community college may hold more weight with hiring managers than a graduate degree." That is largely because certificates often provide supplementary training on top of a degree, helping to advance or improve an employee's skills in a particular field, or to provide more practical training in an area. This is often the case in computer science fields, where programming training, for example is essential.

Studying to master a particular technology platform, programming language, or technical process may have a higher ROI (return on investment) than a four-year degree in a non-technology subject. This is especially so given the lack of qualified professionals in fields like cybersecurity and data science.

More specifically, Code.org analyzed data from the Bureau of Labor Statistics and reported that while computer programming jobs are growing at twice the national job-growth average, 1 million high-tech jobs will go unfilled by 2020 further highlighting the mismatch between what students today are studying and the jobs of the future. Microsoft co-founder Bill Gates has spoken out about skills required for future success, stating that science, engineering, and economics are essential. Workers with training and expertise in those subjects will be "the agents of change for all institutions," Gates told LinkedIn executive editor Daniel Roth.

Questions surrounding the long-term benefit of a college degree, coupled with a declining high school population are already impacting colleges and universities, according to the National Student Clearinghouse Research Center. From a peak of 20.4 million enrolled college students in 2011, that number has fallen to 18 million by 2017, hitting for-profit universities and two-year programs the hardest. Fewer students are heading straight to college after high school.

Part of the responsibility for the rising tide of students who may be unconvinced that a traditional college education warrants shouldering a huge amount of debt goes to the current higher-education system, which is severely lagging the pace of technology. According to a report by Accenture as reported in *Forbes*, two-thirds of college graduates believe they need additional training to even enter the work world. Higher education isn't adequately preparing students for the reality of today's technology-reliant work.

Redefining How Students Learn

This lack of preparation shouldn't be a surprise given the lack of innovation or evolution in the classroom—the teaching format hasn't changed much, if at all, in centuries. As before, students sit in classrooms facing an instructor in front of the class—the "sage on the stage"—who lectures on the topic of the day and sends them off with homework to aid in recall. Students are generally divided by age, less frequently by ability or demonstrated knowledge of the topic, except in Montessori schools, where students of varied ages learn together and from each other.

Some schools now use tools such as whiteboards and interactive classroom response devices ("clickers") to check in with students on their subject comprehension, but in many schools, that's the full extent of technology adoption. More technologically advanced classrooms may use a flipped model, where the student watches video lectures before class and then arrives ready to discuss the content, but adoption isn't widespread.

Meanwhile, at home, students are using their smartphones to have video chats with friends, watching YouTube videos for fun and instruction, and quizzing themselves using apps like Quizlet and Memorize. The current educational system in the U.S. is falling woefully behind the technology curve, making it much more difficult to prepare students for technology-reliant careers down the road.

Compensation for Expert Residual Labor

Automation has changed skill requirements in virtually every industry, from office management to transportation to agriculture. On some farms, automation is being introduced to address the labor shortage, including in the San Francisco area, where the shortage is as much as 20 percent, according to a recent *Wired* article. When the number of available migrant workers declined, Taylor Farms California invested in robots with water knives to cut lettuce heads—work formerly done by hand. But instead of replacing the entire migrant workforce, the robots work side by side with humans, supplementing the remaining labor force. Taylor has also modified the type of lettuce it plants, choosing to grow a Romaine variety that sprouts more like a lightbulb, with a longer base that is easier for a robot arm to reach and cut.

As the influx of migrant workers continues to decline, because of an aging population compounded by increased restrictions on foreign labor, more robots may be needed. And the skills required to run the farm will shift from planting and harvesting to include managing the technology required to do the physical labor.

This trend will emerge across a wide spectrum of industries, as technology that automates simple tasks requires human support.

The Coming Wave of Labor Syndication

In order to utilize robots to take on work formerly done by migrant workers, companies are breaking down work processes into component tasks. In the case of Taylor Farms California, the lettuce-cutting robot has assumed one piece of a larger process. Other components of the growing cycle, such as planting, watering, weeding, trimming, cleaning, and packaging may be completed by humans or other types of robots. But in order for robots to perform as expected, doing what has been human-only work, humans with tech experience to program them will be required. While there are fewer high-level programming jobs than there are blue-collar roles, workers with specialized tech expertise will do well financially.

This is in part because we're moving quickly to a gig economy, where specialist workers are paid a premium for their skills. As those specialists are hired as needed to complete certain tasks, we're also seeing more labor syndication. An online labor syndicate is a lot like a general contractor, which then farms out separate pieces of a larger task to specialists. Jobs become short-term projects that are divided up into tasks for multiple specialists to complete.

One example of a labor syndicate is Amazon's Mechanical Turk—MTurk. MTurk is a network of knowledge workers—"an on-demand workforce"—available 24/7. It's built around an application programming interface (API) that lets companies add the MTurk technology to their platforms. This human intelligence marketplace allows "requesters" to submit projects and begin to get deliverables completed almost immediately—everything from image and video processing to information gathering and data verification.

On Topcoder, clients post project work that has been sliced and diced into component parts for freelancers to bid on. Each freelancer works independently on his or her piece of the project puzzle, delivering it back to Topcoder so it can be combined with pieces completed by others. Topcoder stitches the work together and delivers it to its client. As in many industries, the most talented, specialized workers on Topcoder earn up to 10 times more than the more generalist coders taking care of simpler tasks.

This informal class system within the programming network is going to become more common across numerous industries. We'll start seeing experts demanding, and being paid, a premium for specialized skills.

The Gamification of Work

Another trend in the work world made possible by advances in technology is gamification, a process that transforms work opportunities into games. Take 99Designs, for example. Clients looking for design services for deliverables that include logos and product packaging announce the project, invite multiple designers to submit a design, and offer a prize to the designer whose work is selected. It's a winner-take-all scenario, with the chosen designer being paid for his or her work and everyone else earning nothing for their effort.

The benefit to the client? Less time invested and more design options. Rather than investing hours in meeting with multiple designers, the client can announce a contest and then sit back to see various solutions participating designers offer.

We're seeing gamification at work and in product development. The creation of user-generated content for online apps is improved by rewarding points and recognition for input. Waze, the community-based traffic and navigation app, gives points to participating drivers who provide input on road conditions and map changes. The more points users earn, the higher their ranking. Although a ranking means nothing—much like the high score on a video game—it's a point of pride that Waze users value, which motivates them to help keep the app up to date.

Salesforce.com, a platform for managing customer relationships, does something similar to encourage use of its software. The company identifies super users on its client sites and rewards them with patches. The goal is to catch the eye of fellow employees, who will then want to know how *they* can earn patches.

It's a game of increasing usage, with party favors that cost the company nothing. And they work. Salesforce attracted 175,000 of its customers to its annual user conference, where it went all out to pump up the crowd about its product.

Other organizations offer high-performance indications that go beyond accumulated points worn as a badge of honor. At one consulting firm I worked with, every employee who billed at least $1 million was given a $2,000 bonus and a hat. That hat was one of the most coveted items in that office. It meant you had skills.

Everyone wanted to win one, to one-up their colleagues and show off their new hat. And in wearing it, they instantly conveyed that they were rainmakers.

At that company, everyone knew that the more they billed, the more perks they could win. Consultants who billed at least $2 million were called on stage during the annual company event and recognized. And both the consultant and his or her spouse were each given $2,000. At $5 million in billings, high-performing employees received a $25,000 bonus and a black American Express card.

Gamification also allows you to reduce the cost of new hires because you can choose highly skilled professionals through gamification on a hiring platform. So, is this the direction work is headed—parsing projects and doling out pieces of tasks to highly skilled technicians, rather than employing full-time workers? Yes. In fact, in many industries, we're already there.

Hard Work Won't Be Enough

As technology and automation eliminate large swaths of knowledge work, there will be an increasing need for expertise in many areas. People with skills will continue to find opportunities to work and those with specialized expertise will be in demand. But what will happen to workers who lack such skills?

They have a problem.

The truth is, even if we gave people a road map of what to do to flourish in the emerging economy, not all will have the capability or IQ to make the pivot. We know this because half the people in our society have an IQ of 100 or less; even with considerable effort, they won't be able to keep up.

Those of you who have seen the movie *Caddyshack* may recall Judge Smails saying, "The world needs ditch diggers, too," when caddy Danny Noonan suggested he couldn't afford to go to college. No one wants to be a ditch digger. The pay sucks, the work sucks, and we really don't need more of them.

Now, I'm not saying that most people are stupid—far from it. What I'm saying is that "regular" people are going to have a harder time contributing meaningfully to an advanced ecosystem. For that reason, I don't see how we're going to be able to avoid some kind of Universal Basic Income (UBI).

People at the top will be able to butter their bread with caviar if they want to. However, people at the bottom, will likely struggle with making ends meet. The people in the middle—most people—will be separated by their attitude and aptitude. I call them the two As; they're the two filters I use in hiring at Rumjog:

Attitude: You need to have a desire to know and be willing to invest in knowing (a.k.a. studying).

Aptitude: You have to be able to "get it" and understand a concept well enough to explain it to others.

The wealth concentration that is coming will allow the top 5-10 percent to experience a level of abundance never before seen in our culture. This segment is the target market for the experience economy—who have all the material comforts they could imagine and will shift their focus to spending on experiences. These are the individuals who have $10,000 to $50,000 per month in disposable income. This segment is already large in major metro areas and will continue to swell as earning power continues to shift to this group.

Workers with this level of income have the aptitude and the attitude to do complex work. Employers with a need for their skills will pursue them, offering higher and higher compensation to tap into their capabilities.

Where the Opportunities Are

The good news is that through labor syndication markets, organizations will increasingly be able to obtain access to workers they might not have been able to afford on a full-time basis, but which become affordable on a smaller scale, by breaking down work into smaller components. Independent contractors can bid on working on certain tasks or certain shifts, and employers can pick and choose who wins.

Instacart, a grocery-delivery service, is a trailblazer in this respect. The company announces available work shifts once a week and contractors in good standing can claim them; those who have received "incidents" have a harder time claiming shifts. Rather than having a supervisor assign shifts to available workers, the platform makes them available and workers take what they want (or can get).

The system typically works well for Instacart workers with solid reviews—their skills are rewarded—and less so for workers who have complaints on their records. Just as specialists in higher-paying industries earn more than lower-skilled workers, the same pattern appears in the general labor pool.

This may be the hiring model for the future and will be be developed in even advanced and high skilled job categories like doctors. The challenge for organizations going forward is determining how they can best take advantage of the opportunities technology is presenting. Given the coming decline in college degrees and rising use of technology tools to complete once-human tasks, how will companies balance the mix of technology and human resources to achieve optimal results?

Some companies are already shifting their human capital away from full-time permanent roles to as-needed, higher-paying consulting gigs. Workers who have the skills and track record of performance are thriving in this environment, while those without them are being relegated to the back of the pack. Rising reliance on technology is causing this upheaval, which is going to become more pronounced as the technology itself becomes more developed.

CHAPTER 6:

Process—Redefining Workflows to Take Advantage of Technology

"Machines are predicted to be better than us at translating languages by 2024, writing high-school essays by 2026, driving a truck by 2027, working in retail by 2031, writing a bestselling book by 2049 and [performing] surgery by 2053. In fact, all human jobs will be automated within the next 120 years."

- Timothy Revell, "AI Will Be Able to Beat Us at Everything by 2060, say Experts," *New Scientist*, 5/31/17

IT'S TRUE THAT, to this point, organizations that have leveraged technology have generally been able to grow more aggressively. Thanks to the power of digital technology, software systems have been developed that automate and complete many tasks faster than humans can. Simple tasks formerly done by humans are increasingly being assumed by software and artificial intelligence, and we've heard for years that the benefit of that shift is that workers in lower-level jobs can be moved into higher-value roles. However, that's happening only in some circles. In others, human roles are being completely wiped out, never to be replaced.

Historically, most organizations have had to take into consideration what human workers are capable of and willing to do. That determined how the business operated. Take store hours, for example. Retail stores are open during the day because that's when people traditionally go to work. It's also when people shop and eat. At night, they sleep. So requiring workers to show up for overnight shifts reduces the pool of employees to draw from, because fewer people are willing to work at that time. Consequently, organizations have had to limit their business offerings—they aren't open at night or have a reduced list of services—since there are fewer employees available then to do the work. They are constrained by this resource called employees.

Human employees also need wages and benefits and time off and federally mandated breaks. Their physiology simply doesn't allow them to work for hours on end without a respite to recharge. So companies have structured their workflows to take into account these workforce requirements.

When Machines Drive Business Processes

With human workers driving the process, it makes sense that companies need to limit how long employees can work at one stretch—doctors in training, for example, are prohibited from working more than 24 hours per shift. That's 8 hours more than the 16 hours they were previously restricted to, which was for the health of both the medical resident and his or her patients.

However, when you flip and replace humans with machines that do the same work, without many of the same performance limitations, the result is almost comical. For example, imagine if email were only available during banking hours, or from 9:00 am to 5:00 pm. The reaction you'd get is, "That doesn't make sense. Why is email open only from 9:00 to 5:00?"

The point is, it's not. When machines are in the lead, there are no such restrictions or limitations on service—*because* people aren't involved in the delivery of those services. By removing humans from the administration of email processing, we can restructure and reimagine what business is and what it can do.

In many cases, humans are the limiting factor in business growth.

Consequently, we have to rethink end-to-end processes that rely on human participation. Companies that are burdened by their existing operations, including their human labor force, are at a competitive disadvantage.

Take the airline industry, for example. When the airlines were being beaten by upstart discount airlines in the late 1990s and early 2000s, they started to create their own low-cost brands, to see if that would address the issue. This strategy was much like what automotive brands did to move upmarket, by creating luxury divisions, such as Toyota's Lexus and Nissan's Infiniti lines. In the airline industry, United Airlines created Ted.

Ted began service in 2004, primarily to compete with low-cost Frontier Airlines. Likewise, Delta established Song. The established airlines thought they could compete with the discount brands by building a stripped-down organization, and they were wrong. The new airlines were able to be competitive initially, primarily because the new planes they purchased had much lower maintenance costs. But as the planes aged, those cost savings evaporated. Ted discontinued operations five years later, in 2009, unable to make a profit.

In this instance, there were few opportunities for cost-cutting because of the high labor costs. Salaries and benefits for the airline work force made profitability nearly impossible. That is the burden of having people involved.

In contrast, with software running the show, it can work around the clock, doesn't go on strike, doesn't demand raises, doesn't require insurance or medical treatment, doesn't require retraining, and doesn't get tired. Although finding ways for software to replace people requires a huge investment, once it occurs, the payback is immediate. Organizations can start to rethink the way business is done once software is in place.

Remember how interoffice mail used to be handled? You'd write memos, which were disseminated by hand throughout the company two or three times a day. Or consider US Postal Service mail, which is currently delivered once a day six days a week (five for businesses). Then the fax machine made some mail obsolete, once documents could be transmitted electronically for the cost of a phone call. Then email wiped out most printed memos.

Software is the standard communication tool today. The paradigm has shifted.

Or think about shopping. Amazon has turned the retail industry on its head. Now the answer to the question, "Is the store open?" is always "yes," because Amazon's website is open 24/7/365, and it carries everything from paper towels to computers to clothing, food, trampolines—you name it. Few brick-and-mortar retailers can justify remaining open 24 hours a day because there are too few shoppers to make it worth the expense of its human workforce. But if it's software-based, the expense is next to nothing.

Rethinking Business Processes

Rethinking business processes requires that you break down the existing process, which may have been created to address complexities brought about by human limitations. That is, the work to be done is so complex that we have to standardize it to streamline it and make it possible for humans to manage, or even participate.

Take the workflow of the Department of Motor Vehicles (DMV). When you go to the DMV, you're assigned a particular cashier based on why you're there. If you bought a car and need to pay sales tax, you go to one line. If you're getting a learner's permit, you go to a different line. Trading in license plates? Another line entirely.

Think about how much more efficient it would be to have only one waiting line, with any employee able to handle any transaction. The problem is that would require all employees to be familiar with all DMV processes. That would be difficult to implement. So, instead, the whole process has been developed around the limitations of its workers, who can't master all potential DMV transactions. The DMV has standardized what each worker does and has forced that standardized process back on its customers, who are then inconvenienced by it.

When software is involved, you can introduce an infinite amount of complexity because the software can handle it. In fact, machines are better able to take massive data sets and organize them without human intervention. The machines self-organize. And since people aren't involved in organizing the data or prepping it for the machines to process, you get a very different outcome. In essence, the work is done faster and more efficiently without humans mucking it up.

Many business controls have been developed to try and prevent workers from spending time on tasks that aren't benefiting the company, because people can do a lot of anomalous things that software is strictly prevented from doing. People can cause chaos, even without meaning to.

Within larger organizations, it's very common for middle managers to lose touch with what their team members are doing on a day-to-day basis. They may know what their direct reports are up to but have no idea about the whereabouts of everyone else, what projects they're working on, what hours they're working, how much time they're spending on each task, or much detail at all.

With many companies now allowing employees to work remotely or from home a good percentage of the week, some employers are investing in technology that reports on what workers are doing during the time they should be working. Software loaded onto laptops can use the webcam and keystroke monitors to check on how productive each worker is being. So if workers have an ESPN or YouTube window open on the laptop during work hours, their pay can be docked, because they're not focused 100 percent on their assigned task. Or the webpages that the worker visits during the day can be tracked, to confirm that they're all work-related and not Spider Solitaire. Some software can limit the websites that the laptop can access during the day, too, as an additional level of access control.

An episode of the TV show *Black Mirror*, called "Fifteen Million Merits," depicted a somewhat similar dystopian scene. In it, individuals spent their days earning points to buy food and incidentals by pedaling a stationary bike and watching ads and TV shows displayed on a large monitor in front of them. If they closed their eyes or looked away, the transmission of the ad would stop and they would stop earning points until they paid attention again. If they wanted to skip an ad, it would cost them more points.

It's now possible to use such business controls, which help manage human workers from afar, around the clock. But we still have the issue of cost.

The Higher Cost of Human Employees

Amazon can stay open 24/7 because the incremental cost of staying open is near zero. Software holds down the fort while humans sleep. At Walmart, however, the incremental cost of keeping a physical store open 24/7 is much higher. To stay open, the company pays a team of employees to staff the registers and clean and restock, in addition to electricity, security personnel, and other expenses. The incremental cost there is well above zero.

So why not remove humans completely from the workflow? You lose a lot in the experience, it turns out. For example, when you call a company and are placed into an interactive voice response (IVR) system, where you push 1 for "yes" and 2 for "no," the computer on the other end is progressing through a script. It can't interact with you or handle complex situations that you might try to describe. But if you described the situation to a human, that person could process the information, determine how to address it, and provide a solution. The IVR can go only so far in helping you with next steps because it's programmed only for certain scenarios; if you present a scenario it isn't familiar with, you'll hit a dead end.

However, there are some transactions where eliminating humans from the mix has actually improved the interaction. Take travel reservations, for example. I could either call a travel agent and be told what flights leave when, based on my desired departure date, or I could go to the United Airlines website and see what type of planes are being used for various flights, what seats are available, what the fares are for flights at different times, so that I can pick and choose from among many options beyond departure date and time. For example, I may be willing to leave a little later if the cost of the ticket is 50 percent less, or I might want to leave earlier if there is a meal served on a morning flight. The point is, I can see all my options online, whereas speaking with a human by phone limits the information I have access to. Removing humans from the process provides a richer experience.

Software can also record every transaction to develop a database of your preferences that it can use to guide you in the future. A random reservation agent on the phone doesn't have access to that information and is starting from scratch in recommending potential flights. Granted, if you consistently use the same travel agent, that person can get to know you and where you prefer to sit on the plane or that you like hotels that are off the beaten path. But many services in the modern age are actually better without the participation of humans.

That's not to say that ultimately we want a life without humans—no one wants that. But in managing daily life, you might not want to deal with humans in every situation because they can make business transactions unnecessarily cumbersome. However, by relying on software-based systems to manage daily life, you can also maximize my interactions with the people you care about.

Machine-Reliant Companies

Companies today that are wholly reliant on machines, such as Netflix and Uber, need to restructure themselves to add back the opportunity to interact with humans. These companies were built from the ground up and created with business processes that don't involve human workers. As digital-only companies, they weren't burdened by having to consider human reactions or involvement in those processes. Because when companies have to pivot from the old to the new, from analog to digital, people involved in that shift resist change and the results are suboptimal. When humans see they will be negatively impacted by the coming changes, they make an effort to preserve their role, or any role, even when doing so is not in the best interests of the organization.

Yes, introducing Digital Labor helps companies lower costs, improve efficiency, and reduce cycle time to get more work done faster. But once you do that, you now have the ability to open up whole new markets by adding humans back into the process.

Take Google Duplex, for example. The digital agents on the other end of the phone aren't using a limiting IVR script. They're actually taking in information and providing a custom response based on the data the machine received from the consumer on the line. The potential applications for this type of system are almost unlimited and can help companies improve customer service without increasing cost.

For example, consumer product companies have a limited number of live customer service reps answering product troubleshooting calls. But the company tries to drive more customers to the web to find answers to commonly asked questions because there's no labor expense in providing that information. The company can't afford to pay reps to answer product feature questions regarding a $20 toaster; it's just not cost-effective.

But when you switch to the use of Google Duplex, you can potentially answer nearly any customer question by phone without ever-rising costs. The incremental cost is near zero and the labor is digital.

However, there are areas where humans are going to continue to be needed as part of the workflow for the foreseeable future, and even some areas where they have a distinct advantage—such as in nursing care. Picture elderly people in hospice care. They don't want a robot telling them that everything is going to be fine; they want a human being to hold their hand, talk, and sit with them. Only humans, people, can provide life enhancement to others, by virtue of the innately human feeling of empathy and the ability to connect with others.

People want to be in the presence of other people—that's why we'll spend $5 on a beer down at the local tavern instead of drinking one at home for less than $1. Jean-Paul Sartre was wrong—people need other people.

In a business context, that means you would put humans at the front end of the process, for interaction with customers as needed. They would be the face of the company. And machines would serve as the back office, the administration.

A perfect example of this can be seen at newly renovated McDonald's locations. Once inside the restaurant, customers can choose to head to kiosks to place their food and drink order on a large screen, solo, or to stand in line at the register and speak with a live cashier. Cups are provided so customers can choose whatever fountain drink they prefer, and a single worker behind the counter is responsible for taking food from the grill and putting it on the counter for customers to pick up. Packaging and moving food to the counter is the only step in the entire workflow that hasn't yet been automated; it is the residual part of the process.

Combining Digital Processes to Create New Products and Services

Today, with digital technologies, we're able to do things 1,000 times faster. That means testing and developing new products can also happen 1,000 times faster.

When we look back at Thomas Edison's process for inventing the light-bulb, he tried 1,000 different ways over the course of a year to combine filament, electricity, and voltages until he found that perfect combination that created the lightbulb. Today, that same series of tests and combinations can be done almost in the blink of an eye by comparison.

Because of that speed, people are trying new combinations without much of a downside if they fail. People can be creative without huge, long-term risks. The incremental cost of testing is extremely low.

Take Uber, which we've mentioned a few times. Uber took GPS technology and smartphones and apps to drive location-based services. You can now request a ride based on your physical location. New business models are being developed by recombining digital elements, which is called recombinant innovation.

Look at the potential behind the Apple Watch. Not only can you use it to tell time, send and receive emails, and check social media, but you can monitor your health. We're only a step away from taking the telemetry of the Apple Watch to send it to your doctor so that you can get alerts such as, "Your pulse is running high. What's going on?" Proactive monitoring will soon be possible.

And there are even analog examples that are emerging thanks to new combinations of features. PillPack is another great example. PillPack, which Amazon purchased for $1 billion, solves the problem of improving adherence to medical protocols, especially for elderly patients who can't always read the prescription bottle or who have a hard time opening containers due to arthritis. It also provides routine access to the correct medication at a much lower cost than your local pharmacy. It's going to kill pharmacies. Why would you travel to the pharmacy to pick up vials of pills and then have to split them up and divide them by day when you can subscribe to a service that mails you your pills packed in a ribbon, potentially the next day.

That's an example of combining a few technologies with automatic pill dispensaries based on available data. It's not complicated or high tech, but it's changing how medication is purchased and delivered. And it's removing human beings from the process of delivering that medicine.

The entire work process is being transformed to eliminate the need for analog labor—namely, humans. The first step in the process was automation to simplify the workflow. Time-motion studies were conducted to identify extraneous movements that could be eliminated to improve efficiency and productivity. Next came widespread automation across the organization, introducing technology to assume tasks formerly done by humans. Today, we're grappling with how to automate parts of the workflow that seem like they can't be automated—tasks that humans seem to need to perform.

When the system becomes automated, process roles shift from standardized to customization. That is, once we've streamlined the process to achieve automation, we'll switch back to individual customization.

Take the Apple iPhone as an example. The process to build an iPhone is now largely automated and standardized, but how consumers use the device is totally individual and customized. Apart from the capability to call, text, email, or take photos, users can also download an almost infinite number of apps tailored to their interests and needs. They can also protect their devices by incorporating thumbprint verification.

In some companies, the work process varies by geography. This is certainly true at one medical device manufacturer; the work process in the US is very different from how the same task is completed in Latin America or in Europe. Billing, for example, has variations based on where the product is located, from where it is shipped, and which location gets credit for the sale.

Amazon Prime is another example of a standard work process that can be customized on the customer's end. As a member of Amazon Prime, you can buy what you need whenever you need it and take advantage of free shipping. You could buy something different every hour and it would start to arrive in two days in separate boxes. Prime members don't have to meet the minimum $35 order value to qualify for free shipping, so they don't need to compile an order of several items like non-Prime members do. Non-Prime members need to plan ahead. Amazon has the work process automated down to the last mile.

The Digital Transformation Is Underway

As we look at digital transformations involving Digital Labor, what we are really seeing is the replacement of human middleware with software. You may recall that middleware is software that provides services to software applications beyond those available from the operating system. It can be described as "software glue." In most cases, middleware facilitates data exchange between programs. For example, middleware may use data from customer service platforms in the accounts receivable systems. Human middleware is when humans perform this function instead of software. Think of examples when talking to an airline reservationist on the phone. They log into one system to get your frequent flyer information, into another to check flight availability, and a third to be able to issue refund or billing adjustment.

Historically, human middleware has been used to interface with, integrate, combine, discern, and interoperate systems and processes. The human approach to these functions ranges from the simple (logging data from one system into and another system) to the complex (evaluating an insurance claim for fraud). As software advances and Digital Labor performs these human middleware functions, both simple and complex, humans will be displaced from the old jobs.

But the jobs that are impacted are not impacted in a strata, or in a set sequence; we're not starting at the bottom and working our way up to the top in a methodical sequence. Jobs are being eliminated all over the place, in no particular order.

Several years ago, Johnson & Johnson developed a machine called Sedasys. The machine was designed to perform the work of anesthesiologists in certain routine operations. Broadly speaking, the role of the anesthesiologist is to sedate the person as little as possible while at the same time keeping them free from the stress of a surgical procedure. They monitor the signs of stress like respiration, heart rate, and blood pressure. They use this information to dose the patient with a sedative to keep them unconscious while the surgery is being performed, but not put the patient into a coma. J&J's Sedasys machine would perform this function with a machine instead of an expensive anesthesiologist. The machine would use the same patient data as the anesthesiologist and administer the dosage to the patient in the same way. Theoretically, this would significantly lower the cost of many procedures, as the anesthesiologist is one of the most expensive doctors in the hospital.

In 2016, J&J pulled this machine from the market, more for hospital politics than whether the technology worked. However, this example dispels that notion that only low paying routine jobs are at risk from Digital Labor, as evidenced by the Sedasys machine in this case. All human middleware is subject to automation, eventually.

When we see functions that were performed by humans get replaced by software, we are seeing the beginning of a digital transformation of that function. Every time a human is involved in performing a function in a workflow, it is much slower, more expensive, and more prone to error than when software performs the same task. If workflow were a highway, human work would be like a red light on your journey. In between "red lights," you would race at machine speed, only to wait for a human approval or for someone to get around to performing the next step. If we can reduce enough red lights, the workflow can be transformed.

For example, the process of making a restaurant reservation on Open Table requires no phone calls, no waiting for the person who can check to see if they have a table at your time, no spelling your last name to the host—none of that. Now take the Open Table example to its logical conclusion—many, many functions and tasks performed by humans are can be eliminated in the same way that Open Table removed the human functions of taking a restaurant reservation. And this is just the tip of the iceberg.

CHAPTER 7:

Technology—Developing a Roadmap for the Future

*"Our intuition about the future is linear. But the reality
of information technology is exponential, and that makes
a profound difference. If I take 30 steps linearly, I get to 30.
If I take 30 steps exponentially, I get to a billion."*

- Ray Kurzweil, American inventor and futurist

WE HEAR A LOT about people, process, and technology, in that order, as the essential elements of business strategy. Yet, in truth, we generally pay much more attention to technology than people and process.

Technology is the star of the show for several reasons:

- Technological innovations are central to our culture and the primary driver of improvements to our standard of living. When you consider innovations as varied as computers, TVs, smart phones, advanced cars, food production and distribution methods, and modern medicine, to name a few, it's easy to see how our standard of living has leapfrogged what it was even one or two generations ago.

- Technology has become a model for how problems get solved in new ways. Take a look at Netflix, which now delivers movies to our TVs via live streaming, or Uber, which delivers a car and driver wherever you are in minutes, or Waze, a crowdsourced traffic platform to help drivers navigate the roads quickly with the fewest roadblocks or police encounters.

- Innovators that sell technology have a vested interest in promoting it to the masses, encouraging adoption as the silver bullet that will solve their problems.

Technology has transformed how we live, work, and play in linear and nonlinear ways. Every few months, technology makes incremental or linear improvements—adding individual features to overall capabilities. Once in a while, technology makes a giant transformative step forward, a.k.a. a non-linear improvement, which radically alters the way we live. However, to enjoy both the incremental and transformative improvements to technology, we must adapt the way we work, live, and interact with that technology. So while technology is center stage, there are many other things to consider if you want to drive real impact in the way we live.

In the business world, technology can often get too much attention and focus. Before businesses start to deploy disruptive technologies, they need to start by first talking to people and learning what's going on in their businesses. What problems are they encountering? How have they been addressed? Then, it is just as important to look at their processes. How does work get done? And, finally, how can technology be used to solve these issues? Technology is not the end product; it is the means to solving problems. It is a merely a tool in the toolkit.

Yet if you ignore technology or resist it, it will be at your own peril. Striking a balance between early technology adoption and sitting on the sidelines waiting for others to blaze the trail is an art, not a science.

In many areas of technology, the pace of change is moving too fast to keep up or stay current. When technological solutions are surpassing each other every few months, focusing on one or more individual technologies at a time as the solution to challenging business problems will become extremely frustrating—and expensive. However, when you move early *and* get it right, it can be a game changer.

Take a look at Apple's iPhone as a principal example. The first iPhone model, released in 2007, was revolutionary, "a breakthrough handheld computer," said the *Wall Street Journal*. *Time* magazine called it the "Invention of the Year." The phone-email-instant messaging-music playing-camera device changed how, when, and what people communicated forever. The bar for phone design was raised into the stratosphere. When the iPhone 2 came out the following year, it further expanded the features in the phone, improved the camera and battery life, and offered a larger storage device. Later models added improved device protection, camera quality, and storage, along with never-before-seen payment capabilities, voice-to-text, Siri voice search, and facial recognition as security, among many other new capabilities. With the release of each successive model, consumers came to expect groundbreaking features that almost require them to invest in a new iPhone.

Once consumers experience performance or service at a higher level, they come to expect it everywhere. The bar is raised for everyone serving that market.

Thanks to Amazon Prime shipping, we now come to expect that online purchases will ship for free in 1-2 days. With Netflix and On-Demand programming, we expect to be able to watch the next episode in the series and not wait until next Thursday at 9:00 PM. With broadband wireless internet, we now expect high-speed untethered internet access everywhere. Does anyone still remember the dial-up modems and searching for an analog phone line to connect to AOL? (Ask a 15-year-old, and he or she will not know what you are talking about.)

Expectation levels are being reset continuously as technology progresses every year.

Look around your house and survey the technology. Do you even have a VCR anymore? Who has videotapes? Maybe you have a DVD player and library of DVDs? But now you can stream any movie in high-definition from one of the many streaming services like Netflix, Apple TV, or Amazon. Do you have an answering machine for your home phone? Do you even have a home phone that's a landline? Answering machines have been replaced by voicemail and home phone lines made obsolete by ubiquitous mobile phones. Are you old enough to remember phone books and the Yellow Pages? Internet search replaced these old services years ago.

In all areas of technology advancement, expectation levels are constantly being raised. This applies to all types of technology.

The constant up-leveling of features and capabilities of smartphones prompts consumers to replace last year's model, which is certainly good news for Apple and Samsung. The bad news is that such frequent technological advances cause speedier obsolescence for products that were but a few months ago the latest and greatest innovation. Who has a pocket digital camera anymore?

These familiar consumer examples help relate to an even bigger problem for large-scale corporate technology deployments. It is one thing to buy a $500 digital camera and then have the next Samsung Galaxy smartphone have a better camera, making your digital camera an expensive paperweight. It is quite another issue for large corporations, which are investing hundreds of millions of dollars in technology with very high stakes.

The constant and rapid expansion of technological capability makes it very difficult to invest large amounts of capital into any one iteration of technology to own it. Firms are better off renting technology as a service. You buy the service that includes the underlying technology and let the service provider maintain the latest and greatest. If they do not, you switch services without losing your investment. This way, you can remain flexible in the deployment of these technologies, so that you can later adapt as things continue to change and evolve. You don't want to be married to, or heavily invested in, a costly platform that could end up holding you back. That limits your flexibility.

Flexible Technologies

The most effective way to embrace technology in the enterprise is to create a framework that is flexible and highly adaptive to the ever-changing landscape around us. To do this successfully, you must: 1) recognize that many new technologies are moving to a consumption model whereby users pay only for resources used and 2) focus on data strategy and assets.

Technology companies are becoming aware of the business preference for renting, so they're increasingly providing the capability to rent. We're seeing this in the "as a service" trend that has emerged. There are platforms as a service, data as a service, software as a service, etc. But companies increasingly don't want to be tied down to their technology. When you jettison the ongoing responsibility or liability, you change your capital footprint, and when you change your capital footprint, you have a lot more agility. If you reduce your balance sheet of assets and liabilities and reduce your capital exposure, you're much more agile, more flexible, and more open to new strategic directions because you don't have to carry those assets to the next business decision.

When you own technology, it is a capital asset on your balance sheet and your business functions are, to an extent, required to use this technology—good or bad—to perform work. In contrast is a utility—something you buy, like electricity or water. As a business owner, you need water and electricity to run your business, but you don't create a water department or an electricity department. You really only need access to it. So, instead, you buy it from the utility because it's delivered at a commodity base. Setting up your own utility would be cost-prohibitive as well as unnecessary.

Many technologies are shifting to a utility model. Cloud computing is turning data storage, data center computing, and software management into something you buy as a service. Amazon Web Services generated more than $25 billion in revenue in 2018 and is still growing like a weed. Microsoft's Intelligent Cloud business unit, which includes its Azure Cloud Computing platform, is worth more than $35 billion. These firms and others are turning data computing and storage into a utility that you "rent," rather than owning it yourself.

The Gates Are Opening

Once firms start to shift their computing operations into a cloud computing architecture, it is much easier to leverage interactions with other similarly situated platforms through open standards. Open platforms that are cloud-based and allow other systems to share and exchange data in a secure and reliable manner are the future of technology. API stands for application program interface, which is the location where software platforms and components meet and talk to each other; it's a gate. And there are rules, or protocols, about how information is shared through that gate. I liken it to a border crossing. And where those border crossings used to be like private clubs, where only certain people could access them, they're now becoming public or open to new members. Now data is being processed and exchanged in new ways that were previously impossible when the gate was closed. This new data exchange is driving a whole new wave of innovation.

The GPS (global positioning system) is a prime example. When you have a GPS system on your smartphone, it is shared with a Google utility that takes that data about your location and shares it with Google through an API. What comes back is a dot or a mini image of you displayed on a map, to represent your current location.

But that's not all. In addition to seeing your own geographic location on a digital map, you can also see what's around you. That Google utility can take your GPS data and provide you with information about traffic patterns, gas stations in the area, and hotels, for example. It can also tell you what the price of gas is at each of the service stations near you, and how far off your current route each one is. So whether you use Waze or Google Maps or Apple Maps, each is a utility that takes the raw GPS data, processes it, and then presents it in a way that is more useful for you.

Taking GPS and map data on a smartphone one step further and combining smartphone payments and a mobile application called Uber, you now have a company that is worth $75 billion and redefining the way we think about transportation.

These kinds of utilities are going to be driving business innovation across a wide range of functions and industries.

Take human resources (HR), for example. Let's say I want to hire Karen as a new employee and she needs to be taken through our employee onboarding process. Today, thanks to the availability of HR utilities, I can send the employee onboarding utility her full name, social security number, job title, and start date and what I'll get back is a set of instructions for her about her office assignment, her benefits, her options for health insurance, her login information for the intranet, etc. All the steps she needs to take to get squared away at work are all done for me, her supervisor.

Contrast that with the old way of approaching the onboarding process. In the past, as a company grew it would look for ways to automate processes like onboarding by building its own homegrown system. So you might decide to build a system that takes four data points—such as social security number, job title, start date, and salary—and have it crank out the necessary steps for getting the employee set up and able to contribute. In the interests of saving money on paying an outside developer to create such a system, companies would try and do the work in house. The problem was that it could take a significant amount of unbillable time to design and develop such a system, which might not actually pay off in the long run. It doesn't really make sense to build your own onboarding system unless you know you'll be hiring hundreds or thousands of employees in the next few years.

Small companies may approach the situation by manually onboarding each new employee, which is time-consuming but better than building an entire automated system for the two employees to be added to the payroll this year.

Wouldn't it be more efficient to simply leverage a well-tested software utility that delivers employee on-boarding? How about employee terminations? How about other common functions, such as accounting and finance? I am not talking about a software tool that the firm must purchase, install, and operate. I am talking about buying a utility, meaning a service or an outcome—that is what utilities are.

Once these large utilities hit the market to solve large problems and processes, they can then move down market to solve similar problems on a smaller scale for small businesses. Going back to our GPS example, only the military and major corporations had access to GPS data they were permitted to analyze and use. Now anyone has access, which means anyone can create new utilities to process raw GPS data and create new systems. That creates efficiencies that allow us, as humans, to do other things with our time and money.

Which is another way of saying that you don't need to own technology, but you do need to be in a position to consume it. This requires creating an enterprise architecture that leverages advanced capabilities on a consumption basis and has the ability to shift as the market shifts.

It is critical to think of the technology as a utility you use, versus a core capability you must own. With a utility, you focus on "what," not "how." When you own and operate a technology, you must focus on "how" as it relates to "what." In most cases, this is a waste of time and money. More important, focusing on "how" means that you are not spending time on more strategic endeavors. This is a huge opportunity cost for many firms.

Several years ago, I bought a desk at Costco for a great price. It came in four big boxes and required assembly. Once I got home and unpacked the box and looked at what was required to assemble it, I was not happy. I called the manufacturer's 800 number and was connected to a live person. "How long will this take to assemble?" I asked. The agent asked, "How many people are helping you?" This should have been an indication that I was in trouble. I said, "It's just me." The retort from the agent: "We recommend two people for the assembly and it should take 4-6 hours." I called a friend for help. It took us closer to 8 hours, and I wasted a day and a favor from a friend. From now on, I will not assemble anything—it is a waste of my time and I would rather be doing something else. The great deal on the desk was ultimately a terrible deal.

A firm buying a large ERP software platform from SAP or Oracle is the corporate equivalent of me buying a desk from Costco that requires assembly. The firm shouldn't do it. Buy the outcome as a utility and do not waste time or money on the hidden costs of assembly. Oracle has recognized this and is shifting its model to sell more utility and less software.

To reiterate, with a utility, you care only about how well the utility processes the inputs and creates the outputs.

A flexible technology strategy involves the following:

- Enterprise architecture that shifts definable input/output into callable cloud-based functions
- Separated systems: systems of record and systems of engagement
- Infrastructure that is bought instead of built
- Rigid and efficient systems of record
- Adaptive and customizable systems of engagement
- Technology lifecycle management and its needed integration with enterprise strategy and change management

Innovating at the Edge

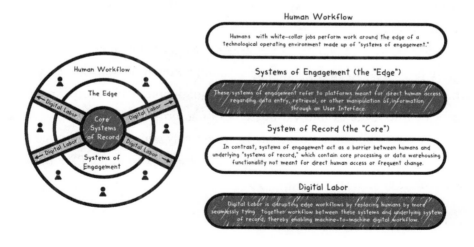

Systems of Record vs Systems of Engagement

As shown in the graph above, there are two types of IT systems in any business: systems of record, called "Core," and systems of engagement, called "Edge." Systems of Record are typically in the back office, or transaction-related. That's where information about payroll is, for example. It holds data. Systems of Engagement are the systems you use to access and analyze the data in the systems of record; they're what you would use to analyze payroll data for the state of New Jersey, for example.

Ideally, the two systems are separated to create stability in the overall operations. Systems of Record are the foundational systems to a business or business process. Systems of Engagement sit between the Systems of Record and the users who engage with the business process, such as mobile apps and web pages.

Most innovation is happening with Systems of Engagement, versus systems of Record. Essentially, innovation is changing the way people interact with business processes by changing the systems that they actually use, which are the Systems of Engagement. The System of Engagement is where people start using the information gathered from the System of Record, such as getting a stock price, reading the latest news, or posting on a social media platform. Users rarely, if ever, have access to Systems of Record. For example, I can change my Netflix playlist, but I can't change the library of available Netflix shows.

Most of the innovation in the area of Digital Labor focuses on reconfiguring Systems of Engagement *or* creating automation software that uses the existing Systems of Engagement instead of people. This is software using software and leads us into various types of automation of knowledge work around the Systems of Engagement—essentially replacing the human-to-computer workflows with computer-to-computer workflows. The impact, when done at scale, is immense.

Technology Impacting Knowledge Work

Let us break down the various types of software automation of knowledge work. Earlier in *Digital Labor,* we talked about the Rumjog Automation Maturity Model, which laid out a way of assessing how companies have deployed automation within their environment. There are three main types of technology that are impacting knowledge work today:

- Automation and robotic process automation (RPA)
- Artificial intelligence (AI) and machine learning
- Data science, which will become quantum computing

Automation and RPA

This type of technology involves automating tasks using software that was formerly done by humans. These are typically simple functions, such as balancing a checkbook.

AI and Machine Learning

Artificial intelligence (AI) is thought of as "the ability of a machine to perform cognitive functions associated with human minds, such as perceiving, reasoning, learning, and problem solving," according to McKinsey's report titled "An executive's guide to AI." Recent advances in AI have leveraged machine learning to apply the power of digital platforms to process massive data sets. AI can currently analyze data and report observations about patterns, while machine learning can analyze the data and take it a step further by making predictions and forecasts and providing recommendations on how to achieve set goals given its forecasts.

Data Science and Quantum Computing

While automation, RPA, AI, and machine learning process vast amounts of data, data science deals with what to do with the ever-growing amount of data. It has to do with extracting that needle in the haystack, that one relevant fact or figure from an ocean of data.

That piece of data is what we term a "signal." The signal is that piece of information we want to find. When you have large data sets with a low signal-to-noise ratio, you have millions of data points and only one I'm looking for, so the ratio is something like 1,000,000:1. It's extremely tedious to start at the top and move toward the bottom in search of this one piece of data that you're after. So you have to be smart about how you approach the search. Rather than systematically searching from start to finish, the analysis might exclude certain data sets until you can home in on a small number of facts or figures that could be what you're after.

We're seeing regular advancements in how that search happens, and it's getting much more efficient, even as the size of that data ocean continues to expand. Quantum computing is what is going to make a successful search possible, but it's likely several years away.

What all of these technologies have in common is their reliance on data, lots of it. Too often, firms are so focused on deploying the latest technology that they ignore their data strategy or fail to align data policies to their technology. It's like investing in an expensive fighter jet without considering where you'll get jet fuel and pilots to operate it. That jet becomes an expensive toy not unlike many technology initiatives that focus on technology alone.

A Flexible Data Strategy

When companies start to operate more at machine speed, the best decisions are made based on data—that is, they are data-informed. Which means that no matter the level of the enterprise—whether executive, managerial, supervisory, or associate—the people making decisions have access to the data they need to make an informed decision. If I've asked for sales projections for next year, for example, the team crunching those numbers needs to have access to historical data. Without it, the team can't produce reliable forecasts. The forecast will be intuitive—more of an educated guess than anything else, because there is no data on which to base it.

High-frequency trading on Wall Street is an example of data-driven decision-making. That's all it is—data-driven decisions. It takes real-time data on what's happening in the markets, processes it, and acts on it, by initiating trades based on the data. And those traders are making money hand over fist.

But data-driven decision-making can benefit any kind of organization. We worked with a consumer products company that frequently had to ship products in temperature-controlled vehicles. Temperature-controlled trucking is much more expensive than regular trucking, so limiting its use impacts profitability.

The company was surprised to analyze its data and discover that managers were shipping products in temperature-controlled trucks because they weren't sure whether the products required it. That was costing the company hundreds of thousands of dollars in added shipping costs.

Their solution was to analyze more data. They input information about weather, routing, delivery time, and the product itself to determine how it could be shipped. Sometimes the system determined that, based on the route to be taken and outside temperatures, the product could be shipped via non-refrigerated methods. In other cases, forecast weather and potential delays led to recommendations for refrigerated shipping. Because they were more precise about it, the company lowered its shipping costs dramatically with the use of machine learning to process multiple data points.

That is decision-making done at the ground level, but it has just as large an impact at the CEO level. When Netflix decided to start developing its own programming, it looked at the company's data. Netflix had plenty of data about which movies people watched, how long they watched, which movies people binge watched, how their movie selections were similar to other selections, and plenty of other details. Then the company looked at a customer's library and that of millions of other Netflix subscribers and found that if you watched the British *House of Cards*, you also liked David Fincher movies and Kevin Spacey shows. So Netflix decided to make an American version of *House of Cards* with David Fincher starring Kevin Spacey.

Netflix put $100 million behind that data-driven decision and totally changed the company's trajectory. That $100 million investment grew to 100 times that—to more than $10 billion in market value—on top of a few Oscars.

When we start making data-driven decisions, we make better decisions. Companies that make data-driven decisions—rather than gut decisions, experiential decisions, or intuitive decisions—will outperform all the latter.

Data is at the heart of advances in AI, machine learning, and advanced analytics platforms.

Breaking Down a Data Strategy

What, exactly, does a data strategy involve? Let's use the library as an example. The typical business executive may have 200 books at home on his or her bookshelves but has probably read only a fraction of them. But those 200 aren't the only books that executive has access to—he or she can borrow from the local public library or buy virtually any book currently in print through Amazon. What people own and what they have at their fingertips are two different things.

The same is true of companies. They have a lot of data within their systems. It sits on their shelves. And, best-case, they may use 25 percent of what's sitting inside their offices in multiple departments.

But, again, when you add the metaphorical library and Amazon—what companies could get if they wanted—they're probably using less than 1 percent of available data to make their business decisions.

As consultants, when we begin working with clients, we ask to look first at the data they have immediately available. We call that *the enterprise data catalog.* Then we look at what they could have—what's available to help drive business decisions.

That then leads to issues surrounding the politics of data, or who owns or controls which sets of data. And we frequently discover that the CFO owns the financial data, the HR director owns the employment data, and so on. To get a handle on who has control of, or access to, which data, we lay out a

RACI (Responsible, Accountable, Consulted, Informed) chart. Such charts provide a way of looking at the roles people play and who owns what data.

It can get complicated quickly, especially when regulatory compliance is added to the mix. There are HIPAA laws in the US that determine who can access health care data. The new GDPR regulations in Europe determine who can be contacted by online ventures, just as the US Federal Trade Commission oversees what companies are required tell consumers about affiliate relationships. There are many restrictions and you need to understand them, as well as what the opportunities are, who has the decision-making right, who can publish the data, who can read it, and who can edit it, among many other decisions.

It's a complex process, but if you get it right and then codify that map of what's available, you can then exploit the data for decision-making purposes as well as revenue generation. And that all starts with navigating the politics of data, figuring out what you have, what you could have, what you could get, and what the rules are around all of the data forms that would enable you to get access and use it.

For example, if your business has an electronic door lock on the front door, you can track who comes in. If you have RFID readers with keycards, you can track who goes in and out at all times. And if you have cameras in the elevators, you can use facial-recognition technology to track where people go most frequently. There's a lot of digital exhaust, or extraneous data, generated in addition to the data created for the express purpose of employee attendance tracking. With that, you can cross-correlate a lot of the data to see when employees enter the building, where they spend most of their time, and when they leave, to calculate exactly how long they're actually sitting at their desks working. Or whether they're working a full eight hours, even though that's not the stated purpose of the data collection.

Monetizing the Digital Exhaust

When you get disciplined about organizing and capturing all of the digital exhaust coming from your corporate platforms and combining it with outside data and analytics, you have the ability to generate additional revenue streams.

Let's use Amazon as an example. Amazon sells millions of products, and it uses the data gathered about what products you search for and what you buy to offer you additional purchase options. The site already offers product bundles, suggesting other add-on or complementary products to go with the items already in your cart. To take it a step further, Amazon could start investigating why you bought what you bought—what made your product choice a better option for you?—and then start to tie in ecommerce to that why, for more product and service recommendations that are supremely relevant.

In addition to Alexa being a piece of technology that can control the electronic devices in your home, Alexa is a device that also gathers data about what you're thinking and talking about. Android devices, Apple devices, cable set-top boxes, and other consumer electronics also do this. And then the companies sell that gathered data to other companies interested in getting their ads in front of people talking about problems they solve.

For example, if you and your family start discussing buying a new big-screen TV for your family room, it's very likely you'll start to see ads from TV manufacturers and electronics retailers in your social media feed. Although some consumers are caught off-guard by ads that are very relevant to their purchase decisions, it's also a consumer benefit. You give Alexa access to the conversations you're having and, in return, you get product and service recommendations that are highly relevant to your current life. You benefit, but at the potential loss of privacy.

Likewise, consumers who send their DNA to companies like 23andMe to learn more about their ancestry also potentially benefit from the sharing of that data. Consumers can elect to share their DNA information with others. I did that and learned that I had five brothers, two sisters, and numerous cousins I never knew about, because I was adopted. I've been able to connect with them thanks to 23andMe. So, yes, I made my DNA data public, but I also benefited from it directly.

In most cases, making your data public, or sharing it through your purchase decisions, won't result in any earth-shattering news, but it may shape the information you're presented. For example, if you buy camping equipment, you may start to see information on campgrounds in your area—something not physically related to what you bought but that might support how you're going to use it.

Architecting the Future

The future business architectures that are going to enable the continued innovation and evolution of Digital Labor are centered around the notion that technology is part of the solution, but it is rarely 100 percent of the solution. Organizing your business into standalone technology silos is the old way of organizing—that apps group, the data center group, the network organization, etc. The new way of organizing focuses more on end-to-end business processes that are set up to be streamlined with technology—customer order-to-cash or hire-to-retire business processes.

When you organize by relevant business process, you start solving problems using technology, rather than deploying technology for its own sake. Instead of a hammer that looks for the nail—that is, technology looking to be used—we focus on improving our processes leveraging technology. The key here is where the organizational focus is.

When firms start solving problems using technology, we'll start to see the big impact to jobs at scale. However, if you lead with technology, change will happen much more slowly, because technology, in and of itself, doesn't solve the problem.

As soon as firms organize around process and use technology to solve labor problems, there will be major impacts to the job market. Currently, we're seeing high demand for employment as a result of companies employing expert labor to help scale technology. The expert labor is scarce, so experts are making lots of money deploying advanced technologies, which is lessening the jobs impact at the moment.

But once we start solving problems with technology rather than deploying technology in and of itself, change will be rapid and far-reaching. And remember that digital solutions scale very rapidly once they are operational.

PART III:

What's Coming Next?

CHAPTER 8:

The Coming Transformation of Business

*"Longevity in business is about being able
to reinvent yourself or invent the future."*

- Satya Nadella, CEO Microsoft

IN EARLIER CHAPTERS we discussed the trend of replacing human workers with software. This approach leads to reducing headcount and cutting labor costs, since software doesn't require any kind of salary or benefits package. It is essentially free labor.

By itself, software replacing people is transformative with respect to the old business models. However, it doesn't stop there. The transformation opportunities come in waves, with each wave of transformation building on the prior wave. Ultimately, this leads to business models that are entirely re-imagined and, in many cases, these new business models will be unrecognizable from the where they are today.

Three Waves of Change: Defensive, Offensive, and Re-imagining Business

Technology deployment that is focused on making existing operations more efficient and more profitable is essentially a defensive strategy. For example, McDonald's deployment of self-ordering kiosks in an effort to reduce labor costs is a defensive measure to address rising labor costs that are the result of new minimum-wage laws. Similarly, retail stores are introducing more self-service lanes to reduce cashier costs, and even toll roads are leveraging E-ZPass to automate toll paying and reduce the need for human toll collectors.

This defensive approach to using advanced software platforms to make processes better, faster, and cheaper is Wave 1 in our model for creating value using Digital Labor.

In our model, there are three waves of value. With each successive wave, the business impact gets bigger—in some cases, much bigger.

The Waves of Value Creation

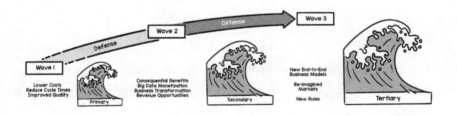

Wave 2 is the offensive strategy. To use a sports metaphor, as with any good game plan, you must deploy both a defensive and an offensive strategy. The defensive strategy is centered around improving efficiency and cutting costs, while the offensive strategy is about creating new revenue—or scoring points, to extend the sports metaphor. Essentially, the goal of the offensive strategy is to derive value from the operation by selling more, selling new, and selling different.

In the case of the McDonald's kiosks, because the company has a digital platform replacing its low-cost labor, McDonald's can now execute a sophisticated offensive strategy of cross-selling or upselling each customer by suggesting add-ons to an order. These suggestions could be routine in nature (e.g., "Do you want fries with that?"), or they could be sophisticated, based on AI and machine learning, about which suggestions are the most effective. That could be based on what the customer orders, time of day, weather, or location, among other factors (a late-night order might warrant a question about a dessert, while snow falling outside could lead to a hot chocolate suggestion). McDonald's can do this in the same way that Amazon suggests other items related to your purchase.

This Wave 2 offensive strategy drives new revenue into the system that you would not likely get from trying the same strategy with a low-wage cashier. Going further, McDonald's can introduce incentives for customers to identify themselves during the purchase through digital loyalty programs: for example, you could sign in with your McDonald's membership number and get special offers just for you, from discounts to free items. With this information, McDonald's can start the process of data mining your identity and expand what it means to cross-sell and serve you as a customer. This is highly profitable and the future of the retail restaurant business. For McDonald's, this is an offensive strategy, not just cutting costs, but rather creating new revenue from existing business activity.

Once a firm deploys the first two waves, then there is the opportunity to deploy the third wave. In the three-wave model, it is usually in the third wave that we see the most profound impacts on the system. By deploying Waves 1 and 2, firms have the ability to re-imagine entirely new business models. This re-imagination of potential new Wave 3 business models is because Wave 1 and 2 converted the old legacy, human-based model into one that is more digital. The re-imagination in Wave 3 is no longer constrained by what humans can do. From 24/7/365 open for business, to high-frequency trading on Wall Street where stocks are traded multiple times per second, Wave 3 is more about what is possible for machines and software. This is where things get really interesting.

McDonald's is still in the early stages of its Wave 2 deployment. If it were to venture into Wave 3, what would it look like? Perhaps McDonald's could think about the gamification of its business—for instance, *"Buy stuff at McDonald's with your loyalty card, get points for discounts on gas or other services."* Perhaps the company should consider partnering with Tesla to deploy car-charging stations, create a sit-down café, and upscale the whole brand. This would be good for Tesla and good for McDonald's. McDonald's has the real estate and Tesla needs ubiquitous charging stations for the growing legions of electric cars on the road. Or perhaps McDonald's creates something more than a sit-down café— maybe there is some retail aspect, or other services, such as car-washing and detailing. These are just ideas, and the purpose of Wave 3 is to entirely re-imagine the business model without the constraints of the past. For McDonald's in Wave 3, it is about moving beyond selling fast food.

Most digital transformations that are happening today still reside in Waves 1 and 2. There are examples of industries that have gone through all three waves and have redefined who they are as a business. Let's go back to our favorite example of Netflix to illustrate the movement through the waves:

- **Wave 1—Defense:** Netflix lowers costs by eliminating stores and mailing DVDs to customers. Then it gets rid of late fees by moving to a subscription model. Then it lowers costs even more by leveraging broadband technologies to stream movies, so you don't have wait for the mail. Better, faster, cheaper.

- **Wave 2—Offense:** Netflix mines user data to create deeper, richer experiences. By developing an advanced recommendation engine, people come to Netflix and watch what is suggested, instead of seeking out a particular movie or show: *"What should we watch? Let's see what Netflix recommends."* And it is surprisingly very good at picking new content for a particular individual. Membership explodes.

- **Wave 3—Re-Imagined Business Model:** The recommendation engine now knows everything about you, from your viewing habits to your attention span to the type of content that will keep you on the platform. The company invests in original content, spending $100 million on *House of Cards*, which is wildly successful. Netflix follows up with dozens and dozens of new original content programs, investing billions of dollars. Membership explodes and prices rise. Netflix, after Wave 3, is no longer a video-rental company; it is one of the most powerful studios in Hollywood, winning its first Oscar from the Motion Picture Academy in 2019.

There are other examples, but not every industry has good Wave 3 examples. How will we think of McDonald's if it successfully executes a Wave 3 strategy? Who knows? To help identify the elements or building blocks that make these waves possible and start to profile the changes happening in various industries and job markets, we leverage the elements of Peter Diamandis's 6 Ds of exponential growth, described in the book he co-authored with Steven Kotler, *Bold: How to Go Big, Create Wealth, and Impact the World.* The three waves in the Rumjog model are loosely based on Diamandis's 6 Ds, which are:

- **Digitalization**: Digitizing a product or service involves converting it from analog to digital technology, or from a physical product to an information-based one. That is the start of the exponential growth curve, says Diamandis: "Something digitized can be replicated and transmitted for a near-zero marginal cost."

- **Deceptive Growth**: Early on, growth can be occurring so subtly that it doesn't look like progress at all. Diamandis uses the example of the first Kodak digital camera, which produced 0.01 Megapixel images. "As it grew from 0.01, to 0.02, 0.04, 0.08 ... they all seem like zero," he says. Meaning, progress was barely perceptible, or deceptively small.

- **Disruptive Growth:** Disruption then follows deceptive growth, which eventually becomes quite evident. Diamandis points out that the original 0.01 Megapixel image that doubled 30 times grew 1 billion-fold. "That first 0.01 megapixel Kodak camera is now generating a 10-megapixel image," he points out, which leads to "the complete dematerialization and demonetization of film photography."

- **Dematerialization:** During dematerialization, products and services are converted into a digital form, such as software or an app. For example, the GPS device you used to attach to your car's dashboard for navigation has been replaced by a built-in navigation app on your phone. Or the desktop scanner you used to copy and transmit documents no longer exists because you can use a scanner app on your phone as well. An additional gadget isn't needed, following dematerialization.

- **Demonetization:** Demonetization follows dematerialization, because once a product or service has been converted into a digital form, its cost of dissemination is near zero. For example, digital photography has nearly demonetized the field of photography, since cameras and smartphones can now snap quality photos that can be shared digitally or printed.

- **Democratization:** "As products and services dematerialize and demonetize, they become available to billions of users across the planet," says Diamandis. Nearly anything available in digital form can be accessed by consumers anywhere in the world with a connection to the internet, whether it's a digital form of a magazine (like Forbes.com), social media platform (think Facebook or Instagram), or educational program (like MOOCs), to name just a few.

At Rumjog, we have taken these 6 Ds and organized them into a framework that shows how they relate and progress through the three waves of digital transformation.

The Waves of Value Creation

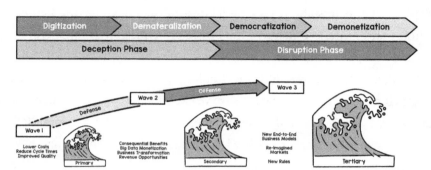

As the waves build, it is important to understand that each of the building blocks (i.e., the 6 Ds) that fuel the waves continues to build and lead to larger and more impactful waves.

When we think of impacts to the labor markets with each successive wave, especially the knowledge worker, we can start to identify emerging trends for each wave. We can expect to see changes with respect to wages, the usage of expert contractors, and within the entire crowdsourcing or gig labor markets.

Job Impacts from Wave 1

Most companies and industries are still in the middle of deploying Wave 1 strategies. That is, they are focused on lowering costs, reducing cycle times, and improving quality through the implementation of technology. This is a daunting task when the delivery of services relies heavily on knowledge workers to perform both back-office functions (such as finance, HR, and legal) and customer-facing functions (such as sales and customer service).

The first challenge to deal with is change. People resist change, especially when they see that the potential change is going to impact their jobs. When we discuss this, we have a saying: "The turkeys don't plan Thanksgiving dinner." Why would they? It is human nature to resist change. This makes the deployment of cost-saving digital technologies very difficult to implement at the outset. In fact, one reason companies outsource their operations in today's market is less about seeking labor arbitrage (e.g., paying people less offshore) and more to outsource the hassle of helping their employees cope with and accept the change.

In Wave 1, the sweet spot for technology to replace people is in the area of replacing human middleware. As we've explained in previous chapters, for many knowledge workers, their entire jobs are to act as human middleware. Just about every knowledge worker job has large amounts of human middleware tasks to perform every week.

The sweet spot of Wave 1 is the automation of human middleware. Why is this the prime target of Wave 1 technology deployments? Think of the building blocks from the 6 Ds. Wave 1 is formed and fueled by digitization and dematerialization. Digitization is the transformation of physical products into a digital or electronic format, while dematerialization removes any connection to their physical form.

For example, with digitization, we convert workflow from paper or analog processes to digital-based workflow: from memo to email; from paper receipt to electronic ledger; from verbal to electronic. Wave 1 is also fueled by dematerialization—converting the physical to virtual. Digitization leads to dematerialization by its very nature, but it takes things one step further. The answering machine becomes voicemail. The fax machine becomes a PDF document in email. The hard disk on your computer becomes cloud-based storage.

Digitization and dematerialization set the groundwork for human middleware functions to be replaced with software middleware. Think of memo filing in the analog world—there were cabinets and storage, a filing system, and a process for storing and retrieving a document. Today, the email programs do all of that at zero marginal cost, zero cycle times, and zero defects. Nothing new here, but now apply this to every possible human middleware activity and you see the same Zero Concept emerging in a variety of knowledge worker jobs.

In Chapter 3, we discussed the Rumjog Automation Maturity Model (RAMM), where we broke down a variety of emerging technologies that are behind the automation of knowledge work, as shown here.

Rumjog Automation Maturity Model

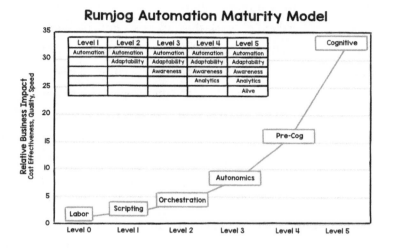

For basic human middleware functions, scripting and orchestration can automate many routine tasks and workflow, including simple data entry, ledger reconciliations, simple customer service inquiries, report generation, and even analysis functions. This should be of no surprise to anyone, but what may be of surprise is the scope and capability of these automations.

In 2019, the hot topic in this space is RPA, Robotic Process Automation. RPA is Level 1 and Level 2 in the Rumjog Automation Maturity Model. The two leading RPA software firms in the industry are UIPath and Automation Anywhere, which together have a market capitalization of more than $10 billion as of early 2019. Five years earlier, in 2014, the companies were virtual unknowns. The rapid growth suggests the scope and breadth of RPA in the market is much more than most people think.

RPA is a set of software scripts that run on the same workstation that humans use every day. Essentially, a software program is installed onto a computer or virtual machine and "wakes up" when it is triggered or scheduled. RPA is designed to run specific commands and perform keyboard-based inputs within applications used by knowledge workers. These RPA scripts, or bots, interact with their environment through the front-end user interface, filling in forms, clicking buttons, and navigating portals originally designed for human use—the only difference being that the bots move much faster than humans and they do not make mistakes. Their only limitation is in the inherent rigidity of the scope of work they address. For the most part, RPA bots cannot deal with environments that are too dynamic but rather rely on rules-based, repetitive, stable processes that can be codified easily.

RPA is simple, cheap, and easy to implement, with the major benefit to organizations being the increased speed of executing repetitive middleware activities, as well as the reduction in labor costs from fewer humans being involved in the back office. The impact that RPA can make to an ecosystem is magnified when there are very complex *and* routine rules-based work to perform. Historically, firms have thrown lots of people at the problem. These people need training and oversight to ensure that they follow the policies and rules for a function such as claims administration. RPA can automate much of this work and, once it is set up, it requires no training and follows the policy and instructions without waiver.

A great illustration of this comes from a project Rumjog worked on with a past client in the medical device space. The company's shared service center was staffed with personnel solely dedicated to handling incoming claims from its customer base. Claims is an area that touches almost every part of a business: customer service and sales teams manage the incoming claims and complaints; the quality department investigates broader issues that may be apparent in each product that may have caused the claim in the first place; finance teams must handle any reimbursements; and the supply chain must be notified regarding returns or new shipments that need to be facilitated. This is a perfect stage for RPA to shine—a process with many handoffs between teams, many systems that need to be accessed and reconciled, and a convoluted workflow of reviews and approvals that need to be orchestrated smoothly together. It sounds complex to automate, but this use case is still rules-based and repetitive and has a direct effect on improving customer experience.

At Rumjog, we built a series of cloned bots to deal with this claims administration workflow. This project addressed the work of 18 full-time personnel with bots that cost less than $25,000 to produce and less than $10,000 a year to maintain. The 18 full-time personnel cost a lot more.

Wave 1 is huge, and we're already seeing companies ride it. Amazon is a groundbreaking example. It digitized the product catalog and dematerialized the store, because the company doesn't have any brick-and-mortar storefronts. By operating digitally, Amazon has lowered costs, reduced cycle times of product delivery, and improved the quality of access to goods and services. It also shares information gathered from its customers to help other customers make smarter choices about their purchases, thereby reducing its return rate. Amazon's foundation as a business is Wave 1.

There are many other examples, but Wave 1 is the first step in a multi-step process that converts human labor to digital work, followed by more significant changes to how we work and live. Later waves make use of the digital exhaust—data created as a byproduct of digitization—by creating new revenue-generating products and services.

The job impacts from Wave 1 will impact tasks more than jobs. Jobs will mainly be impacted when Wave 1 is done at scale and the firm just needs fewer people to perform work across the system. There will be fewer overall jobs rather than specific jobs being impacted. Some specific jobs will be affected, and these are jobs that are almost exclusively human middleware-style jobs. In the airline industry, for example, the job of airline reservation agent is directly impacted by the deployment of airline and travel websites that completely replace their job. But more often than not, the wake of Wave 1 creates new jobs—although the number of jobs, the skill sets required, and the location of the jobs are usually quite different from the jobs displaced.

Job Impacts from Wave 2

Wave 2 builds from Wave 1 and signals a shift from a defensive to an offensive strategy, by leveraging the digital workflow or by monetizing the digital exhaust created in Wave 1. Leverage comes from taking advantage of the fact that workflow is now digital and dematerialized and we can now run the business differently. Data monetization or exploitation comes from leveraging the digital output or digital exhaust of the system as a new revenue opportunity.

Let's look at a leverage example. Remember when only travel agents or airline reservation specialists could make plane reservations? We've touched on this example before. You had to go through them to reserve a seat on a flight; there was no other way. However, once the workflow of booking flights was digitized, airlines were able to provide websites to their customers to make their own reservations. Now, airline reservations can be made by anyone at any time. Access to flight information is widely available through the internet; there is no proprietary platform you must pay to use. It's free and available to anyone. You can choose to go direct to the airline on its corporate website or through a discount middleman such as Expedia or Trivago.

Websites moved to airline mobile applications, and the check-in and boarding process was streamlined. Mobile apps started upselling extra baggage allowances, extra legroom, and entertainment options for a flight. The reservations systems also offered tie-ins for hotel and car reservations that are associated with air travel. Beyond saving money from a Wave 1 strategy, this Wave 2 leverage created a whole new revenue stream for the airlines. This new Wave 2 revenue is now essential to their financial success and future product innovation.

Let's look at a data monetization example. Travel websites go beyond just giving you the information you asked for. They use the massive amounts of data they have collected on people who have already traveled to where you are going to also suggest hotels you might like to stay in, cars you might want to rent, and activities and excursions you might enjoy while you're there. They take the digital exhaust from previous customers and package it to entice you to do business with them. This creates whole new revenue streams for the airlines that are essential to their business model.

Airlines can even go one step further and harvest the airline passenger information and sell it to interested parties: hotels, car-rental companies, restaurants, tour guides, etc. While there are privacy rights and issues to be worked out, the point is that this data is valuable to potential parties whose business interests align to the type of data exhaust that comes from digital workflow in the airline industry—therefore, it will be exploited. When you click "OK" just to get past a pop-up screen on the airline's mobile site, you just agreed to allow them to monetize your data. If you had an attorney review what you just agreed to by clicking "OK," you might be surprised. It is not all bad. In fact, it is mostly a good thing, as you become the co-beneficiary of this exploitation if it is done well. If you need an airport transfer from London Heathrow to the center of London, you may find that the airline provided your information to Heathrow Express and there is a 30 percent promotional discount, saving you both time and money.

You might be thinking that this is nothing new: airlines have been doing this for years. The purpose of the airline example is to provide you a familiar framework to relate to, but this is happening across many other industries and services.

Let's look at an Amazon example. Right now, I'm able to order almost anything I might need from Amazon's website 24/7, thanks to its digitization. However, Amazon also takes information it has collected from other customers to recommend additional products I might need to go with my order, based on what others have found they needed. Have you bought a 4K TV? Amazon might suggest you also buy an extension cord or HDMI cable to go with it. Are you buying a MacBook Pro? You might need a USB adapter, which Amazon is happy to suggest and sell to you.

Wave 2 makes possible the creation of new business opportunities based on new data available through digital exhaust. It's the potential for new revenue streams—it is profound, builds from Wave 1, and is often more impactful to the business.

The jobs impact from Wave 2 is more substantial than from Wave 1. As business models shift through the first two waves, they essentially pivot from analog or legacy business workflows to a digital business model. This digital business model relies much less on people to perform day-to-day work and much more on people to process, analyze, and pursue the opportunities that emerge from a digital operation. In other words, more experts are required and fewer "arms and legs" are needed in the workforce. This has huge implications on the labor base. Not all of the "arms and legs" people can pivot into expert areas, such as data analytics, business analysis, and innovation that moves the firm into Wave 3.

The Waves of Value Creation

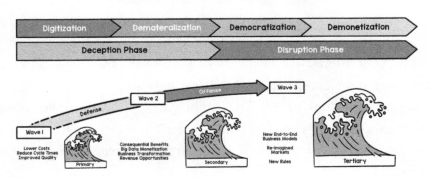

Looking at the 6D framework from above, as we complete Wave 2, we are exiting the deception phase of digital transformation. Why is it deceptive, especially from a labor perspective? The main reason is that the overall impact on jobs could be neutral or even net positive. The new jobs that get created precede the old jobs that are getting lost. While there are localized displacements in the job markets, it is often argued that people just need to be retrained to move into the better new job being created. This would be true if there were no Wave 3, and precisely why the first two waves are the deceptive phase. At Rumjog, we would say that the mantra for Waves 1 and 2 is, "The early bird gets the worm." Essentially, the firms that get Waves 1 and 2 operational are set up for the transformational Wave 3. And Wave 3 can be a tsunami, not only for jobs, but for entire business sectors and industries.

Job Impacts from Wave 3

Wave 3—the next wave and the final wave in our model—is the biggest wave. It's the tsunami. Where Wave 2 could be several times bigger than Wave 1, Wave 3 can be profoundly larger than Waves 1 and 2, in terms of business impact and most important, in terms of jobs, and specifically, in terms of the job of knowledge worker. Wave 3 is the point at which business models are completely reimagined.

After Waves 1 and 2, you have digitized and dematerialized. You lowered the costs of product and service delivery and monetized the data and its resulting exhaust. The business that emerges from Waves 1 and 2 relies much less on human labor to perform work, scale the business, or process change. This is profound. Why?

If I do not require additional labor, or a very small amount of labor, to run or scale my business, then the margins on new revenue and additional revenue is extremely high. The margin on the next customer at Netflix, once its platform is in place, is above 90 percent. This is the essential nature of digital business models—that is, once the platform is up and running, the cost to provide service to the next customer is close to zero. Economists would call this a zero marginal cost structure. Additionally, digital business platforms are much easier to change, modify, and upgrade than their analog counterparts. Why? Once people are removed from the delivery of service, no re-training is required to change or experiment with digital variations of the service. The combination of high margins and low cost of change for future innovations are some of the ingredients that fuel Wave 3.

In Wave 3, we are now able to democratize our business—essentially, serve many more people regardless of location, time of day, income strata, or any other characteristic that blocked market expansion. Amazon is open 24/7, whereas the mall closes at 9:00 pm. Amazon can sell to me in New York City, Denver, or Seattle—the mall caters only to those in geographic proximity.

Because the margins are so high, business can then lower the cost of services to reach a wider audience and allow for people to buy their products and services where normally they would not have been able to afford to in the old model. This is the demonetization aspect of the progression and completes the sixth and final of the 6 Ds—the Disruption Phase.

The Waves of Value Creation

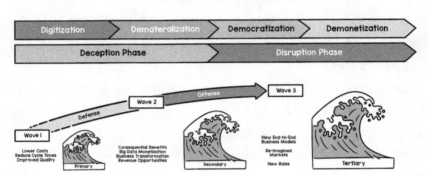

Wave 3 is the disruption phase of the overall wave model that we have discussed as seen above If Waves 1 and 2 constitute the deceptive phase, Wave 3, which leverages democratization and demonetization to completely re-imagine the business model, is the disruptive phase.

In the deceptive phase, we said, "The early bird gets the worm." In the disruptive phase, we say, "The bird is for dinner."

If we look at how Netflix pivoted into a Wave 3 business model, we see it executing democratization by getting the Netflix app on every SmartTV and platform. It works on cable systems, smartphones, tablets, iOS, Android, on the web—it is everywhere. Netflix also demonetized the service and made the price affordable for a family: four screens of up to 4K streaming for $15/month. That is less than $4/screen-per-month for what amounts to countless hours of entertainment. In contrast, one video at Blockbuster was $4 and you had to drive there to get it, if the store even had what you wanted.

Now comes the transformation. With a digital platform and exploding subscribers from democratization and demonetization, Netflix was able to use the data or digital exhaust from users to reveal incredibly valuable insight that otherwise wasn't available. In the prior chapter, we talked about how in 2013 Netflix used digital exhaust to inform their first investment in original content with the American version of *House of Cards*. In 2018, Netflix was using digital exhaust to spend $8 billion on original content and has 700 original TV shows and movies in its portfolio. At the time of Netflix's original *House of Cards* investment of $100 million, Netflix (on a split-adjusted basis) was trading around $10/share. As of mid-2019, it traded at more than $370/share. Netflix's market capitalization went from just over $4 billion to more than $160 billion in the course of 6+ years.

This new and transformative content model has been so successful, other large firms including Google, Amazon, and Apple are trying to get in this game. Netflix continued to push the boundaries and changed the rules regarding show releases and started releasing entire seasons at once. "Binge-watching" is a term that emerged around the time when Season 2 of the *House of Cards* was released. Netflix released the entire season at once on Valentine's Day 2014 and saw an eight-fold increase in downloads vs. Season 1. This broke with traditional models that would release one episode per week that networks like HBO and Showtime largely still adhere to. With this new model, Netflix essentially created the concept of binge-watching and changed the way people watch long form series.

Traditional studios and broadcast television networks have been devastated by the rise of Netflix and others in this new model. Unlike Netflix, broadcast television must take into account the interests of advertisers. And since shows are broadcast at a set time on their channels, the content must have some broad appeal. As a result, broadcast television basically sucks. The networks pump out reality shows because they are relatively inexpensive to produce. They are hard to watch and even harder to imagine who is watching *Housewives of Death Row Inmates* or *Naked Celebrity Chefs*. If you haven't unplugged yet, you soon will. Who would have thought this 10 or 20 years ago? This is the power of a Wave 3 transformation.

The jobs impact from Wave 3 transformations is much more profound than Waves 1 and 2. The primary reason for this is that the transformation tends to wipe out competition in the old markets. Whether it be Netflix killing broadcast television; or such platforms as Facebook, Twitter, and Craigslist killing newspapers; or Uber killing the taxi/limo industry; digital market transformations tend to result in a winner-take-all outcome. In cases where it is not winner-take-all, then there are typically only a few winners. These winners employ far fewer people than the industries that they replace.

As more and more industries and sectors of our economy go through the three-wave digital transformation cycle we have laid out, there will be far fewer jobs than there were prior to the transformation. Certainly, some new jobs will be developed, but how many and with what skill sets is unclear. My guess is fewer but higher-paying jobs. In any case, the demise of the knowledge worker is upon us over the next 5-10 years.

To get a sense of that, let's look at some wave progressions in other industry sectors.

Wave Progression in the Financial Markets

Let's walk through the wave progression in a few sectors of the financial markets. For example, in stock trading, Wave 1 shifted the process from manual to automated and sped up the cycle. Formerly, a customer phone call initiated a stock trade, which then had to be handed off on paper from broker to trader on the stock exchange floor. In contrast, in Wave 1, brokerage firms digitized the process, automated it, and put it all online. Now a customer can log into his or her account, initiate a trade, and see it happen in real time seconds later. There is so little lag time between placing an order and execution that the stock price has little chance to change much.

In Wave 2, brokerage firms can now focus less on executing stock trades (which are now completely automated) and more on selling services to clients. Brokerage firms can take market data and offer paid subscriptions, or run analyses and make buy/sell recommendations that encourage clients to act at optimal times, earning them more money. Clients can also be given additional capabilities, further automating trades to set up buy and sell orders at specific price points, including calls and puts—all of which are hands-off transactions.

Although humans in Wave 2 still initiate stock purchases and sales, in Wave 3, humans can be completely removed from the process, because of high-frequency trading. In fact, high-frequency trading firms don't need outside clients at all to make money. They can set up sophisticated software programs to watch market moves and buy and sell stocks in microseconds, taking advantage of small movements that net profits hundreds of times a day. The firm itself consists of a few managers and banks of computers. Long gone are the days when high-paid (human) traders raked in high salaries and bonuses on Wall Street.

Wave Progression in Health Care

Health care is also experiencing its own waves of value creation, thanks to Digital Labor. In an ongoing effort to reduce costs, improve the quality of care, and lower labor requirements, health care practices have been moving to electronic medical records (EMR). Patient records have been digitized and saved in the cloud for easy access by any medical professional from any-where in the world when needed. That was Wave 1.

In Wave 2, thanks to access to new insights about patients gleaned from reviewing all their electronic records, health care organizations can start to make recommendations based on patterns identified. For example, a doctor might see that a Keto diet has helped patients quickly drop some pounds, or that a particular vitamin regimen helped reduce stroke risk, which the doctor can then prescribe to patients at risk for stroke. Being able to tap into millions of new data points creates new information that can be sold to customers, in the form of prescriptions, supplements, and fitness routines.

Diabetes care is experiencing upheaval as a result of Wave 2. Type 2 diabetes patients used to take insulin as a protocol when their blood sugar was up. Now doctors are recommending lifestyle adjustments to prevent patients' blood sugar from spiking or dropping in the first place, reducing reliance on insulin. So, companies that previously sold insulin pumps and protocols around insulin delivery for sugar-level management are now competing with businesses that are selling lifestyle adjustments as a treatment option. Firms that integrate wearable computers devices like a Fitbit or an Apple Watch created applications on the smartphone that started to gamify behaviors to provide proactive positive feedback to Type 2 Diabetes patients. This prompted more exercise, fewer bad food choices, and led to an overall healthier lifestyle, thereby avoiding the need for an insulin injection.

Then Wave 3 comes along, which involves selling life extension, rather than disease management. It's a totally different model of care that is causing massive shifts in how medicine is practiced. Life extension is the polar opposite of disease management. With disease management, you go to the doctor when you are sick or have a problem. With a life extension approach, you are constantly and proactively monitoring your vitals to optimize health, thereby driving life extension and higher quality of life as a result.

The life extension transformation of healthcare is a big move away from reactive disease management. The business of healthcare changes radically. Disease management is episodic with price points of $100, $1000, and many $1000s per event like an office visit, a minor procedure, or major hospital stay. Life extension models are not episodic, they are regular and constant with prices points of $0, $0.05, and $1 for things like steps walked, activity report, or minor diagnostic like and at home test strip. But this is just the beginning, for less than $100 you can get your DNA tested or test the length of your telomere chromosomal caps. The telomeres test will give you biological age and compare it to your chronological age. You could be 40 years old but have the biology of a 30-year-old or a 50-year-old. Getting insight into this with credible data, can then lead to making lifestyle choices that optimize health and avoid the onset of chronic diseases that plague our healthcare system. This is the future and it is an emerging Wave 3 transformation.

When this transformation occurs, how many jobs that are inextricably linked to the disease management side of health care will be lost when people are healthier and need less chronic care? What new jobs will be created when more people pursue a life-extension protocol for their health.

Wave Progression in Transportation

An industry where we've already seen and heard about upheaval is automotive transportation. Tesla has already made great strides in removing the human driver from the process of navigating a vehicle, and the Google car is certainly in the works, making possible a self-driving car in the very near future. It's already in testing. That was Wave 1.

In Wave 2, we saw data about driving habits and patterns yield new business opportunities, especially at Uber. Where Uber started by providing consumers with transportation from Point A to Point B on a just-in-time basis, the company then took all the data it had gathered about where people go most frequently and monetized it, rolling out Uber Eats to deliver restaurant meals. It's another way for Uber drivers to supplement their incomes by providing a related driving service. Instead of calling an Uber or driving to a restaurant to pick up a Chinese meal, hungry consumers can now use Uber Eats to have their Cashew Chicken delivered directly to them. That's where we are now, at Wave 2.

When Wave 3 hits, which will likely be in the next 5 or 10 years, the entire automotive transportation industry will be transformed. A declining number of consumers will go to the trouble of buying and owning their own cars, choosing instead to buy a transportation package from a company like Uber, which will ensure access to transportation whenever it's needed, without all the added hassle of owning, parking, insuring, and refilling the gas tank of your own vehicle.

Some people think it's a fantastical vision, but it's coming sooner than anyone expects. Because once you remove the need for a car in your garage or driveway, there's a domino effect. Not only do you reduce the expense of car ownership, you reclaim all that time spent driving yourself here and there. Some estimates are that we spend as many as 500 hours every year behind the wheel if we drive an average of 15,000 miles per year at an average speed of 30 mph. That's a significant amount of time to reclaim, which can be reallocated to do work, meditate, read, or even nap.

Without the need for a car, you can also turn that garage space into something else—a guest bedroom or home office maybe? Or perhaps you'll use it as a separate Airbnb unit you rent out for added income? Looking ahead, home design will likely evolve to remove the need for a garage and driveway altogether.

On a larger scale, without individually owned cars, there will be less need for auto insurance, gas stations on every corner, even huge parking lots. There will be widespread shifts when Wave 3 hits the transportation sector.

As we mentioned earlier in the book, the most prevalent job in this country is truck driver. Once we cross the tipping point for automated vehicles, what will these people do? While it will be hard to call a truck driver a knowledge worker, the loss of a truck driver's employment follows what will be a similar road map to what will happen to the knowledge workers. Essentially, their work will dry up through the transformation of entire industries. The new industries will employ some knowledge workers, but fewer and generally people with concentrated expertise.

The Digital Agenda Continues to Unfold

As traditional labor and knowledge work is replaced with Digital Labor through the three waves of value, there will be a corresponding need for specific human expertise in many areas. While technology is progressing rapidly, there is a portion of a solution or process that requires a human element.

An Emerging Conflict of Interest: Labor vs. Technology

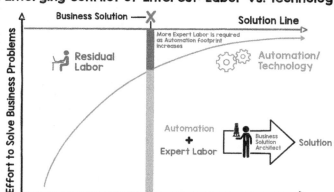

As seen in the graphic above, in the early phases technology replaces the simple and routine knowledge work. As time progress and we move from Wave 1 to Wave 2 and to Wave 3, the resulting residual labor required to complete a transaction or body of work is smaller and much more expert in nature.

The expertise will vary, based on the type of products and services being delivered autonomously, but usually a common element will be having a high degree of conceptual intelligence on the part of the expert. Think of the phrase, "Those who know how, work for those who know why." Digital Labor and the advanced software platforms know "how." Humans, for the foreseeable future, know the "why" element of labor—strategy, goals, planning, etc. We could characterize this as executive skill sets, to an extent.

In some other cases, human expertise could be tied to regulatory or legal frameworks. For example, IBM Watson could determine the diagnosis and treatment of a cancer patient, but IBM Watson is not licensed to practice medicine. A licensed expert doctor, one highly skilled in both oncology and how IBM Watson works, will be required to sign off on any recommended medical treatment. The human doctor needs to understand the types of mistakes or errors that IBM Watson might make based on incomplete data sets, outside factors, or other issues outside the purview of the IBM Watson analysis. This is something that only a highly skilled expert would know.

Another expert class of knowledge work will simply be areas that have yet to be conquered by Digital Labor and AI—perhaps design thinking, fashion, or areas that require a high degree of human empathy in order to work properly. These experts, like the experts in the IBM Watson example, must know their specific area and be considered expert *and* they must know the technology that surrounds their expertise in order to work collaboratively with the technology as it progresses in capability and scope.

For example, think of the music industry and look at the success of DJs like Tiësto, Deadmaus, Avicii, and many others. You may not have heard of them, but these are an emerging set of music stars that can make as much as $50 million per year performing and recording music. They all have, or had, expert talent, but what sets them apart is the ability to leverage technology (synthesizers, computers, mixing software, etc.) in their creative process. They don't sing or play musical instruments per se, they mix and create new digitally produced sounds using the technology and their music dominates the club scene. If experts do not understand the technology, then they are missing an essential element to being an expert in the future Wave 3 transformations.

The last major group of expert labor are the people who can install the Digital Labor technologies in the classic ecosystem dominated by human knowledge workers. These experts need to be polymaths—experts at many things—in order to be effective. They need knowledge of the industry, of a company process, political skills, technology skills, conflict-resolution skills, financial skills, planning ability, etc. No emerging platforms are "plug-n-play;" instead, they require a tremendous amount of management and work to be properly implemented into an existing ecosystem. The lack of true experts worldwide in the space is the key factor affecting Digital Labor adoption timelines in the economy.

Who are these experts, and where will they come from? That is a critical question for all leaders embarking on any digital transformation initiatives. First, companies will look to hire talent in the emerging areas. However, in most hot areas, talent is scarce and expensive. Firms should view this group of experts as seeds to help them with the second and most important and differentiated group.

The second group of experts will come from within the businesses existing labor pool. This talent must be cultivated and curated. They need to be trained, educated, and supported by the business by being rewarded for driving innovative change. The first group of experts (the ones you hire) need to learn your business. They need to learn the specific ways that your firm operates from business processes to the office politics. The second group of experts (the ones you cultivate) already know your business, they need to learn the technology. Think of the first group of experts as those who can give you a roadmap and the second group of experts to help you scale the initiatives.

Consider this metaphor: As we constantly break new ground in the progression of Digital Labor technology and services, we are stepping into a jungle of the unknown. In many cases, it is pioneering work. The experts that we need for this are "jungle guides"—that is, people who have similar experience and are smart enough to apply the old knowledge to the new world without rigid adherence to the old playbooks. In a sense, jungle guides will help you avoid making rookie mistakes, but the jungle is new to them as well.

The expert jungle guides are expensive—too expensive to own or hire full-time, but worth every penny if you rent them at the right time. You would not walk into a jungle without a guide, and you should not move forward with a Digital Labor transformation without consulting with experts who will help you avoid expensive rookie mistakes that could cost your firm time and lots of money.

At Rumjog, we see a future where experts of all shapes and sizes are rented through crowdsourcing platforms. This is the emerging gig economy, and it is not just for Uber drivers. More and more experts (coders, doctors, cyber security professionals, architects, strategists, legacy tech, writers, etc.) are going to rent out their services by the job. Crowdsourcing platforms are emerging in many areas to support this. There are dozens, if not hundreds, of emerging crowdsourcing platforms facilitating the use of expert labor on a gig basis.

Let's look again at the platform Topcoder. There are 1.2 million developers, designers, and data scientists on Topcoder's platform. Most of the people on the platform are augmenting their income and learning. The top 10 percent are making a full-time living, and the top 2 percent are making more money than they ever could working as an employee. They can also set their own hours and are untethered from the corporate 9-to-5 grind. If you want to hire a data scientist as an employee, good luck. They are expensive, and there is no guarantee they will make the impacts you are contemplating. The same is true for cybersecurity: good luck. These are two hot areas where experts are in very high demand, and crowdsourcing offers a new and viable alternative to hiring and employee.

As Digital Labor progresses, there will be more and more classes of expert labor emerging, and crowdsourcing will be one key way to access this talent without breaking the bank.

The Early Bird Gets the Worm

Every CEO and C-suite leader should go through the exercise of thinking through what could happen as the organization experiences these three waves of value creation. Because the waves are coming and how well companies survive and thrive will depend on their ability to spot opportunities.

Most companies today are in Wave 1 or early Wave 2. Few have gone through Wave 3 or even contemplated the implications of wholesale industry or sector transformation. Yet many are unwilling to think beyond Wave 1 and, as a result, they are cautious at a time when it is important to move early. They stay laser-focused on making processes better, faster, and cheaper, and they ignore the coming offensive opportunity that their competitors may already be working on.

And if they get behind, they're going to lose in the long run, because digital models and digital businesses are likely to be winner take all. There will be only one to earn a first-mover advantage, and that one will likely control the industry.

To close this chapter, think of this Rumjog fortune cookie one-liner: "It is expensive to be early, and it could be fatal to be late." Now is the time to act.

CHAPTER 9:

New Business Threats and Rethinking Innovation

"Innovation distinguishes between a leader and follower."
- Steve Jobs

IN CHAPTER 8, we broke down the Three-Wave Model of digital transformation. In Wave 1, the strategic focus is defensive in nature. This defensive technology strategy seeks to lower costs, reduce cycle times, and improve the quality of existing products and services. This strategy allows you to maintain a competitive position relative to others that provide similar products and services. That is the essence of Wave 1, the primary wave. Sure, you can gain a temporary competitive advantage by focusing on improving your existing operations, but Wave 1 strategy alone cannot compete with market-wide transformative changes that are coming in the subsequent waves. To use a poker metaphor, Wave 1 initiatives are table stakes and only keep you in the game.

In Waves 2 and 3, we see the pivot to more offensive strategies, or strategies that help business score more points in the form of new revenues. In Wave 2, there is an exploitation of data from the environment. The digital exhaust that comes from Wave 1 is leveraged in Wave 2 to drive new sources of revenue. In Wave 3, firms look to completely transform their operations and create new markets based on a digital business model.

All three waves are threating the current business ecosystem. The threats span the spectrum from Wave 1 as a tactical threat to Wave 3 as an existential threat to entire industries and markets. Understanding these threats is key to defining an appropriate strategy for your business.

Understanding Supply-Side versus Demand-Side Business Threats

As you think about competitive threats to your business, it is important to distinguish between supply-side competition and demand-side competition. Supply-side competition encompasses businesses that sell similarly situated products and services in the market. Demand-side competition encompasses competitive threats that satisfy the market in a totally different way. Supply-side competition can take some of your customers, whereas demand-side competition can take them all by essentially making your product or service obsolete. In digital market transformations, the impacts to your business can play out very fast due to the nature of digital deployments. Once a digital model is working, it scales with little to no effort and a relatively low amount of financial capital.

Let's look at our favorite example, Blockbuster and Netflix, in the context of demand-side and supply-side threats. When Netflix started to compete with Blockbuster, the competition was mainly a supply-side competition. Blockbuster satisfied a market need for at-home movie entertainment by renting out DVDs through physical stores. Netflix satisfied the same market need by renting out DVDs through the mail. As Netflix's membership for its DVD-by-mail service grew, it became a stronger competitor to Blockbuster's business. But it was when Netflix pivoted to focus on streaming services that it satisfied the need for at-home movie entertainment on-demand and the market for physical DVDs nearly evaporated. The pivot to streaming movies was a demand-side threat to Blockbuster's core business. Like many firms before it and since, Blockbuster focused on supply-side competition and underestimated the demand-side threat from streaming. As a result, it went bankrupt very quickly.

There are numerous other examples of firms getting blindsided by demand-side competition: retail stores versus online shopping; taxi/limo versus Uber/Lyft; Kodak versus digital cameras; or hardbound encyclopedia versus Wikipedia. Demand-side competition often leads to obsolescence of your old business model. Contrast that with supply-side competition, which typically results in only a marginal shift in customer market share. In the digital world, demand-side competition is more likely to be an existential risk to your business. When mitigating the risk from existential business threats, it is not the time to be overly cost conscious, as the stakes are too high. Firms that were wiped out by demand-side competition likely wish they had been more aggressive investing in new technologies and business models.

It is in Wave 1 that you typically find supply-side competition, or competitors working to do exactly what you do but better, faster, and cheaper. Take Amazon. Its products—which were originally books and other media—are the same as the products at Barnes & Noble, Books-A-Million, and The Strand, but Amazon's improved process and infrastructure allows it to sell books better, faster, and cheaper than traditional booksellers.

Or consider CarMax, which has created a central database of more than 50,000 used cars for sale that customers can access and purchase from its 200 brick-and-mortar locations nationwide. No longer are car buyers limited to the inventory sitting on local car lots; now they can shop from inventory across the country and have them shipped in for trial. The technology deployment is allowing CarMax to lower its overall cost *and* make it easier for potential customers to search for a used car. The technology also creates a tremendous amount of data to be analyzed and potentially used in a Wave 2 strategy. What car models are hot? What price points are working? What online pictures are more effective? Is there an opportunity to upsell car insurance in the purchase?

Supply-side competition is a threat to your business in the short-term; however, demand-side competition is a threat to your entire existence. Because when technologies are deployed to solve your customers' problems in a completely new and different way, new business models emerge. This is what happens in Waves 2 and 3. Competitors can go after your customer base and provide a new-and-improved solution to their needs. Once these new solutions are in the market, customers rapidly migrate away from the old business models.

Looking at the photography or camera industry, Nikon is a supply-side competitor to Canon in the consumer market: both companies are selling digital cameras to a consumer market interested in digital photography. However, the quality of cameras in built-in mobile phones, on the other hand, is becoming a demand-side competitor to both Nikon and Canon because the mobile phone is always with you and solves multiple problems at once. Consumers are now able to take high quality photos, edit, digitally store and share those photos with family and friends without buying a camera from Canon or Nikon.

Of course, this evolution didn't happen all at once. Historically, most families owned a camera and households were filled with multiple photo albums. It was the only way to preserve memories of family vacations and major milestones. Today, though, a digital camera or even film, isn't a requirement. A majority of folks today just pull out their mobile phone, snap a photo, edit it real time and either store it online or post it to social media.

High quality built-in phone cameras, followed by apps such Facebook and Instagram, entered the market as an enabler to taking and sharing photos, while film companies like Fuji, Kodak, and Polaroid remained unaware of the havoc such demand-side competitors would wreak. Mobile phones have changed all the rules, making it increasingly difficult for manufacturers to sustain themselves, much less compete.

In CNBC's 2019 article, "How Canon, Nikon and other Japanese Camera Companies are Fighting for Survival in the Smartphone Era," it was reported that "of Japan's eight digital camera makers, a group which includes Nikon, Canon, and Fujifilm, only one posted sales and profit growth in the most recent annual period: Sony. And it was not due to gangbuster camera sales but, rather, the steps Sony took to wedge its technology inside the smartphone market."

Photography has evolved over the years from the art of taking photos to a broader context of creating and sharing memories. Recognizing the quality of the built-in camera getting better each year, it is vital that these companies think beyond their physical products and more about providing consumers with new ways of capturing and sharing meaningful memories. Strategies that explore ways to satisfy customer needs in new innovative ways is what demand-side threat analysis is all about.

More on Demand-Side Threats

Demand-side risks are different from the supply side. Demand-side threats don't compete with your business for market share; demand-side threats eliminate and redefine markets. This can happen through technological advancements (e.g., digital replacing film or email replacing traditional mail) or through creative and new business models. An example of a creative model that can be a demand-side threat is product and service bundling.

Let's say you're considering starting up a new local coffee shop. You may view your competitors as other coffee shops in the area, or cafés that sell coffee, and even McDonald's, which sells coffee in addition to hamburgers and fries. Any business that sells coffee can be considered a competitor. Those are your supply-side threats, because they're already doing what you do and may be able to find a way to do it better, such as Starbucks' aim at the premium market, or creating more convenience for the customer with delivery or drive-thru windows.

It is unlikely that we will see a technology-based demand risk to a cup of coffee (at least, I hope not). However, if your business is about selling coffee like the new local coffee shop, there is a demand-side threat to your business when other unrelated businesses bundle coffee into their product or service. This could be a convenience store giving a free cup of coffee for a fill-up or a retail boutique opening next door that gives its shoppers free coffee just for coming into the store. Suddenly, the product you formerly sold for a few bucks is now effectively free, and your customers are no longer willing to pay for it or take the time to do so. Other businesses are providing your customers with what they need—coffee—in a very different way.

Think about how Netscape got killed by a demand-side threat. Netscape was a great browser, but you had to buy it to load onto your computer, much like you purchased all other software packages at the time. Then Microsoft began bundling its browser with every new computer for free. So, while Netscape may have been a great browser, the need for buying a browser became obsolete when Microsoft made it part of the operating system for all Windows-based platforms. Microsoft including the browser in the Windows bundle killed the browser market at the time.

Companies in all sectors and industries are at risk to demand-side threats at some point. As we look ahead, many companies are going to be surprised by this demand-side competition. We're already seeing this in the medical device market. For decades, companies have sold diagnostic equipment to doctors and hospitals to provide patient healthcare information, such as cancer screenings or blood pressure, for example. But when that data can be derived another way, such as through a watch that continually monitors blood pressure or a free app on your smartphone, the need for that diagnostic equipment evaporates fairly quickly. The equipment may operate just as effectively as ever—there's nothing wrong with it—but patients don't need to make an appointment with their doctor anymore to get that information. It can be delivered to them in real-time at no additional cost, perhaps even with trend data, to spot when their blood pressure spikes during a typical day or week.

Spotting Your Demand-Side Threats

To identify demand-side threats, you need to step back and consider what problem you're solving; not the obvious, stated, problem, but the root issue. For example, selling a car helps an individual solve a transportation problem—getting them from Point A to Point B. Supply-side competitors would be manufacturers of cars, motorbikes, or trains. But demand-side competitors could include mass transportation, such as buses or subways; bike rentals, such as through New York City's Citi Bike program; peer-to-peer ride sharing; or Uber or Lyft.

But an even more subtle demand-side threat would be technologies that eliminate the need for transportation at all, such as high-end video conferencing systems. Skype and Teams and other collaboration tools are killing the travel industry at some level, because there is declining demand for business travel. Why take the time and incur the expense of hopping on a plane cross-country when you can use Zoom for a video conference from your office?

Spotting demand-side threats requires imagination and curiosity. Effective demand-side threat examples are obvious only after the fact. Beforehand, most people generally ignore or cannot imagine the possibility that things will change from what they are or were, to something completely new. This requires some level of imagination. To fuel this imagination, you must be curious about your markets. Why do customers behave the way that do? Why do they buy your product or service? What conditions may change your market in a way that would be a threat to your business model?

If you look at the business model of Instacart, you will see lots of potential demand-side threats potentially emerging for grocery stores. Today, Instacart is an add-on delivery service to a grocery store model. If Instacart grows significantly, it can start to deliver grocery items from its own supply chain and, suddenly, the grocery store loses a significant portion of its customer base. Imagine Instacart partnering with the driverless Uber cars? Quickly, you can imagine the potential demand-side threat to the grocery store business model.

Not having a clear understanding of the business that you are really in is the clearest way to become blinded by potential demand-side threats. Railroads thought they were in the railroad business and not the transportation business and got blindsided by automobiles. Kodak thought it was in the film business and lost out to digital photography. Large retailers thought they were in the "store" business and got wiped out by online commerce. There are many examples both large and small.

These demand-side threats and shifts in the market are examples of offensives strategies, which are transformative to the markets that they serve. They kill off businesses and create entirely new ones in their wake. The goal is to move away from Wave 1 to Wave 2 and then Wave 3. Because Wave 3 creates new capabilities, new products and services, and new markets. The business impact of Wave 2 can be many times that of Wave 1, and the business impacts of Wave 3 are usually orders of magnitude larger than Wave 1. As we said in Chapter 8, Wave 3 is the tsunami.

In Wave 3, the business opportunities often originate from the data generated by digital exhaust, or an indirect byproduct of technology. For example, a microscope manufacturer could package and sell data generated by microscope scans, creating entirely new teaching products that become its own profit center. The DNA test kit sold by 23andMe could package user data and sell add-on services, such as life-extension consulting, to offer guidance in how to act on the genetic data discovered through the 23andMe testing process. Monetizing the digital exhaust is really the goal of Wave 3.

Google has morphed from an online search tool to providing email (Gmail), maps and navigation, news, financial reporting, YouTube, Google Drive to share and store digital documents, and creating Android for free to make it available to other phone providers to further proliferate their products and offerings.

The Inflection Point

But before we get to Wave 3, Wave 2 is the shift from defensive to offensive technology strategies. It is the first of two successive strategies, which provide an opportunity to harvest data and monetize it.

The data from Wave 1 creates Wave 2, with the outcome being Wave 3. The data generated from Wave 1's digital exhaust could be anything from credit card data (such as how much you spend in a month) to transactional data (such as what brands you buy and from where) to user behavior data (such as how often you eat out each week).

Wave 2 is the inflection point between Wave 1 (which is how business has been done and continues to be done) and Wave 3 (characterized by the innovative, completely new business models created from the ground up). In Wave 2, you're making incremental changes to how business is done, keeping one foot in the old while planting the other foot in the new world. Whereas in Wave 3, you're completely overhauling the business.

Another way to view the three waves is that Wave 1 involves digitizing analog operations, creating digital exhaust or data. Wave 2 deals with the immediate consequences of the new data that's been developed, though you're still running the same business, albeit one that is improved from Wave 1. You may change various aspects of the company, such as adding features or changing your pricing model, but it's still based on the original business. And Wave 3 is a new business that may have little connection to the original business at all.

In the prior chapter we outlined how Netflix was able to progress through all three waves, going from a video rental service to a major Hollywood studio in the course of a decade. As firms go through these waves, data in the form of digital exhaust needs to be captured, organized and exploited to drive future value.

Harvesting Data—The Fuel That Drives the Three Waves

Across all three waves, the common element is data. Creating data, curating exploiting data, and developing new data-centric business models. Think of the waves as concepts, rather than mutually exclusive stages.

Even during Wave 1, digital exhaust is being produced that provides the basis for new income streams. That digital exhaust is created when you take people out of the workflow, giving the tasks that were formerly performed by humans to machines. It consists of the readings and information that are created as part of the system as it's completing the assigned work—the telemetry.

In a car, the telemetry includes the speedometer, the odometer, the RPMs, the GPS coordinates, the engine temperature, to name a few data points.

Altogether, that telemetry creates an opportunity to package that data into something new and useful that can be sold.

Progressive insurance company was one of the first insurance companies to roll out a device to track driver performance.[22] It was called Snapshot and debuted in 1998. Since then, the program has evolved, shifting from a program designed to reward good drivers to an effort, starting in 2013, to potentially penalize bad drivers. Allstate's Drivewise program is similar but uses smartphone-based tracking information, rather than a device plugged directly into the car.

Such tracking devices collect a vast amount of information about the cars, the drivers, and even the roadways traveled, which could conceivably be analyzed and used to market new services based on that data. Drivers could be offered safe-driving instruction if a company discovered that the drivers needed it. Or municipalities could be sold data on road conditions, to help track of potholes as they develop.

Google does a similar aggregation and resale of data. The company compiles all of the online searches conducted and then sells that data to advertisers, sharing how often certain keywords and phrases are searched and who's searching for them—for a fee. Frequency of searches also drives up advertising rates. That's how Google can monetize search parameters.

New revenue opportunities are now available to almost any company gathering data about its customers. Instead of simply selling products and services, you can also sell information you've collected about your customers to other businesses. Take hotels, for example. Until the internet, customers had to call an 800-number to reserve a room for a trip, which was then stored in the hotel's database. But now that customers can make reservations entirely online, sharing personal data to hold the room, hotels can now take that information about customers and their travel dates, and sell it to area restaurants and venues, so they can market to arriving travelers.

Many products and services today are "free" in that you can use them without paying for the product or service. Examples are Google search, Facebook, Instagram, Snapchat, Twitter, Gmail, and YouTube, to name a few. All of the firms that provide these free services are in the data business: they provide the free services to create data that they own. You may be use these platforms for free, but *you are* the product, because the companies are monetizing what you do, when you do it, who you do it with, what else you do, where you do it, etc. The analytics these companies run can also determine why you do it, what else you might do, who you are, how much money you have, what your mood is, who you might vote for, etc.

For example, Facebook is free to use, but in using it, you're giving the company ownership of content you create, access to your network of connections, and permission to show you personalized ads. Facebook, Amazon, Google, and Apple are listening to everything you say and looking through your camera to determine whether there is new data that they can curate. If you talk about going skiing to a friend in the presence of your smart phone or other smart device, you may see skiing advertisements in your Facebook, Twitter, or Google feeds. These companies will deny that they are spying, but experience and general observation suggest otherwise.

Not sure? Look up United States Application US20180167677. Or answer this question: How does Alexa work if it doesn't listen to everything I say? It has to be constantly listening for "Hey Alexa … " to know when to actively respond. As it discriminates every word that is said, Alexa will occasionally hear a juicy word like "skiing" and will want to sell that data to ski resorts. If you are planning on going skiing, it is better to get a promotional advertisement for a three-day weekend than a random ad for dog food. Just understand that you have waived your privacy to use these free products and that the incentives to use and monetize the data is huge.

The intent of this book is not to opine on the virtues of data privacy; that is an entirely different topic. We just want you to understand what is happening and why. Data is the lifeblood of these companies, and they want more and more to feed their business models. Data is the fuel that drives the three waves.

A Cycle Develops

As businesses move from Wave 1 to 2 to 3, it's not a linear progression but a cycle. Take Netflix again. It started at Wave 1 as an improvement on the Blockbuster business model, then moved to Wave 2 as it began to analyze the digital exhaust it was producing, and then to Wave 3 with the establishment of a studio to produce shows and movies its data showed would be of interest to its subscribers. That transformation took seven or eight years, and now Netflix is back at Wave 1, working to improve its business model, which now depends heavily on its own movies and series.

Or look at Rent the Runway, the subscription service that sends women designer clothing for short-term use. At start-up, it was focused on giving women designer clothes better, faster, cheaper than traditional retailers. That was Wave 1. Then the business began creating digital exhaust, which it could sell to designers to inform them of the most popular colors, styles, fabrics, and sizes shoppers wanted. That was Wave 2: it's where the company is now. Wave 3 for Rent the Runway could be designing its own branded line and setting the fashion trends, instead of selling into the trend—à la *Vogue* magazine. Imagine Rent the Runway creating its own TV series to drive this fashion curation. The potential outcomes are numerous and will surprise the markets. Rent the Runway is just getting started and may not reach Wave 3. If it does, Rent the Runway will look like a totally different company.

Companies don't necessarily have to start at Wave 1 and progress from there, however. In fact, you could argue that Uber started at Wave 3 relative to the taxi industry, but then is back at Wave 1 as it works to refine its business model relative to competitor Lyft. Then expansion of Uber to other services consumers wanted, such as food, led to Wave 2 and Uber Eats. Wave 3 will redefine markets and solve a broader transportation issue. Wave 3 will include driverless cars and redesigned vehicles. Imagine a small living room of wheels for you to hang out with your friends while you are being transported. Imagine you have a mini-apartment in a shipping container-sized footprint. A driverless truck could pick up your living quarters and transport you on a business trip, a vacation, or a visit with family, without having to sleep on the pull-out couch, etc. It's hard to predict the exact future, but these are the kinds of things coming next, and thinking about them will help spot demand-side threats and opportunities for your business.

The Secret Sauce: Recombinant Innovation

As companies move from wave to wave, there is the potential to combine new models or capabilities to create something never before seen. Mash-ups of technologies are the spark of new inventions. In Wave 2, firms seek to mash up new data sets to drive new insights that can be sold—this is recombinant data. In Wave 3, innovators seek to recombine various business models and concepts to create something entirely new—this is recombinant innovation.

Recombinant innovation has been one of the ways innovation has always worked. However, in the analog world, it can be very expensive to make new inventions or test new business models. Physical inventions require proto-typing and investment in facilities to build and test. Testing new business models (such as a restaurant concept or a new retail concept) can cost hundreds of thousands or millions of dollars. In the digital world, the ability to combine data (versus physical things) or the ability to setup a new digital business model (versus brick-and-mortar business) is far easier on a relative basis. If something digital hits, the payoff is huge.

In 2010, Instagram was started by Kevin Systrom and Mike Krieger with $500,000 of seed funding to test the idea of digital photo telegrams: taking the concept of digital photos and combining it with the old concept of telegrams. In early 2011, less than a year after its first funding round, Instagram raised another $7 million of funding with an implied valuation of $20 million. Just a handful of guys innovating in California created $20 million of value in about a year through recombinant innovation.

One year later, in early 2012, Facebook bought Instagram for $1 billion. In a little more than two years, from ideation to $1 billion in value, just a handful of guys and relatively a small investment changed the way that people share digital photos. Today estimates vary, but it is reported that Instagram, which is part of Facebook, would be worth $100 billion if it were a standalone business. From zero to $100 billion in less than a decade. In comparison, as I write this, General Electric (GE) is worth only $90 billion.

This is why most of today's innovations are focused on digital business models. It's relatively inexpensive to combine data and digital business models in new ways, so people can test digital products and services at a much lower incremental cost. That's essentially what recombinant innovation involves: testing many different digital combinations to see what works and what doesn't. Plant a lot of seeds, and if one or two grows, that results in a big payday that can shift markets.

Innovation and Wave 3

Wave 3 is really where the action is. Instagram was born in Wave 3. It is where new business models are conceived of or completely reimagined. Established businesses need to be constantly assessing the opportunities and risks associated with the Waves in their markets.

To explore the possibilities of Wave 3, businesses need to reimagine how their industry and customers' buying behaviors will develop as the market changes with developments in technology and potential recombinant business models.

Let's look at the health care industry. Health care spending in the US is about 18 percent of GDP, or just under $4 trillion. If you take a look at the chart below, you'll see that is more than $10,000 for every person in the US and the highest in the world. It is almost 25 percent higher than the #2 country, Switzerland.

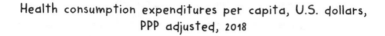

Health consumption expenditures per capita, U.S. dollars, PPP adjusted, 2018

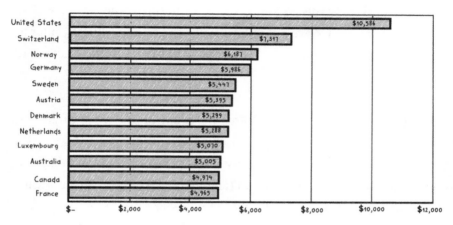

Source: OECD Health Statistics: Health Expenditure and Financing

If any industry is ripe for digital transformation, it is health care. If we apply the Wave Model to health care, it would look something like this:

- **Wave 1:** Using digital technologies to reduce the cost of service delivery. This would include conversion of medical records from paper to digital; automated insurance claims and processing; smart phone appointment and follow-up; hospital administration efficiency; genomic testing; regulatory compliance; deployment of digital medical devices or wearables to monitor patients; to name a few.

- **Wave 2:** Leveraging the data and digital exhaust from Wave 1 to improve patient care. This would include prescription adherence; diagnosis; patient education; insurance claims fraud; gamification of behavior for Type-2 diabetes to incentivize adherence to diet and exercise; using the data to profile trends and epidemics; and developing new insights on lifestyle and disease.

- **Wave 3:** A shift from defensive strategies that lower the cost of health-care (which is essentially disease management in today's market) to strategies meant to optimize health, which shifts the industry away from disease management to one that is more akin to life-extension services. Today, you go to the doctor or hospital when you are sick. Tomorrow, with Wave 3 thinking, you will go to a wellness center to optimize your health. That's a complete inversion of the health care model.

Applying the Wave Theory to health care could be the topic of an entire book. Just understand that the potential is huge for our economy and society. It is a profound shift from a disease-management paradigm (a defensive strategy) to a life-extension paradigm (an offensive strategy). If your business is in a health care-related field, the opportunities are almost limitless to drive innovation and strive for a Wave 3 outcome. However, it is hard to break out of the old models.

The truth is, not only is it hard to break the old models, it can be risky to try new approaches—to be the maverick of your industry. But long-term, it is more risky to stay in your lane and ignore technological shifts that are coming.

Just look at Eastman Kodak Co. Kodak invented the digital camera in 1975 and actively resisted introducing it for fear it would cannibalize its existing film business. While Kodak kept its digital technology effectively under wraps, its competition leapfrogged ahead, leaving Kodak filing for bankruptcy in 2012. The company still exists but isn't known for the digital technology it created.

Similarly, AT&T knew early on about Voice Over Internet Protocol (VOIP) but feared impacting its existing business model by transitioning to it. Executives saw that VOIP worked 20 years ago, but they didn't want to take action to address it or try and compete with it. Instead, they kept their heads down and focused on metered phone service—essentially selling phone calls by the minute, which was the technology of the day. By resisting it, AT&T

suffered a slow death in that market. The AT&T that exists today is actually Southwestern Bell Corporation, which bought the AT&T brand when it went was sold off. It's a completely different company. The AT&T of the 1980s and 1990s no longer exists in its old form, and one of the contributing factors was not reimagining the telecommunications industry aggressively enough because it was safer, in the short term, to stick with the old model.

Going on the Offensive and the Politics of Data

Any company founded today, or tomorrow, or five years from now, is going to be focused on offense, not defense. Those companies will be trying radical new approaches to best the existing companies, which are still focused on using defensive strategies. Companies already in business today are less likely to want to make radical shifts that could cost them their market share. They'd rather continue to defend and at least hold onto the customers they have. Risking the business by pivoting and trying a completely new growth strategy is scary, so they stay the course. They make the safe decision.

What some leaders don't realize is that making the safe decision ensures the company's demise. The business won't be able to keep up with, or catch up to, the new market entrants that are already operating at a level that is cheaper, faster, and better. They're on Wave 1 while startups are starting at Wave 3. A defensive strategy against Wave 3 companies is deadly. It won't succeed because existing businesses may become obsolete, so it is irrelevant how cost efficient they are.

That's in part because Wave 3 companies are capable of moving so much faster. A story out of WeWork is that if someone on the WeWork team comes up with an idea at 8:00 AM in a meeting and four people in the room agree it's good, by the end of the day, that idea has been implemented. Not many traditional Wave 1 companies can compete with that speed.

Further, Wave 3 companies also aren't labor-dependent; they are data-dependent. An offensive strategy in today's market, by definition, is data-centric. It is built around the existing enterprise data, which has been evaluated and reimagined. It is important for companies to lay the foundation for this data centricity in the early stages of Wave 1. They need to identify what data exists that the company has access to. Then, once assessed, the next question is, "Who is interested in this data?" and "What could we do with it?"

An effective Wave Model data strategy goes well beyond creating a list of data in the business and then running some brainstorming sessions. It is much more difficult and complex. A proper data strategy is much more comprehensive and effectively considers the politics of data.

A comprehensive data strategy to drive the Wave model would have several key ingredients:

- **Data Inventory:**
  - Primary Data—company-owned data, such as financial data, customer data, operations data, and research data.
  - Secondary Data—data the company has access or rights to but does not own. Some customer data falls into this category, as well as business partnership data, association data or data that comes from membership or participation in market activities like conferences.
  - Market Data—data that the company can purchase from the market or proprietary research. Analyst reports, third-party customer sentiment data, public demographics and business data, and market data.
  - Derived Data—data that comes from company analytics and data mash-ups. Often this data is the most valuable because it combines insights from primary, secondary, and market data to develop something truly unique.
- **Data Governance:** To effectively drive a data-driven strategy, you need to get data into a form that allows it to be governed across the business. In large corporations, data sits in pockets or organizational siloes. One part of the business does not know what data another part

of the business has. It is difficult to leverage and exploit the data if your data is an organizational mess. Some organizations are addressing this data governance issue by creating a C-suite executive to do this—often called the chief digital officer (CDO). That's a good start, but unless the business changes the paradigm on data ownership and decision rights, then the position is not likely to be successful. That leads us to ...

- **The Politics of Data:** This is the hardest part. The politics of data goes to the heart of the matter for enterprise data strategies:

    - Who owns the data?

    - Who has decision rights?

    - Is there a central authority?

    - Does the firm embrace a data-centric business model? Or do people hold data in their back pocket as a means to maintain organizational power?

    There are regulatory issues to deal with, including GDPR and HIPPA. There are also regional differences on the laws regarding data and data privacy. And there are contractual issues with third-party contracts on data ownership and rights to use. With respect to rights management, for example, non-owned data can be used by the business, but there are limits. In broadcasting, there are Fair-Use laws; technology use involves understanding the patent landscape; and publishing involves copyright laws, among other issues.

If your head is spinning with the complexity of a comprehensive data strategy, then we've made our point. We are just scratching the surface here. This is very complicated stuff, and most firms do not do this well. Digital firms that were born into Wave 3 or have transformed into it have very sophisticated data strategies. Such firms as Google, Facebook, Apple, Amazon, and Microsoft all have very good data strategies, and they have the market capitalization to show for it.

Once a business has its data strategy and the politics of data on sound footing, it now has the opportunity to go on the offensive or to seek out new business opportunities and models that are anchored around its data.

There are many offensive strategies, but let's deconstruct one type of data-centric offensive strategy: monetizing spare capacity in an existing system to users or customers who want to buy something by the drink, meaning as it is used.

In 2004, Amazon CEO Jeff Bezos approved an innovation project to experiment with Amazon computing infrastructure. The company set up an office in South Africa, far from Amazon's Seattle Headquarters. The challenge that Amazon faced was it needed to build out its computer platforms to handle its peak business load in the fourth quarter of the calendar year, when retail shopping is concentrated. By doing this, Amazon had a lot of spare capacity in its platform that was unused for 75 percent of the year. Amazon wanted to re-create a computer infrastructure model that was flexible or elastic to spikes in usage.

Amazon created Amazon's Elastic Compute Cloud (EC2) Services, which essentially launched Amazon into the cloud-computing industry. The genesis of the EC2 (which later went on to become part of Amazon's Web Services, or AWS) was to sell spare capacity on Amazon's computing platform to developers who needed some computing, some storage, and some database services, but who did not want to go through the hassle of building it themselves. That was 2006.

In 2018, 12 years later, Amazon's AWS business unit booked $25.6 billion in revenue on more than 40 percent growth, with an operating income of $7.2 billion. Amazon now dominates a large portion of the cloud-computing market—a long way from selling books.

Amazon's AWS is a simple concept disrupting a very large computer services industry. The simple concept is to create a commercial model that sells or monetizes spare capacity of a fixed asset or platform. The capacity is broken down into small individual elements that are matched to the way that customers want to buy them (versus building those elements themselves).

It's a simple, straightforward concept, but at the heart of it was a data-centric business model and some recombinant innovation to create a highly disruptive Wave 3 business.

Let's look at another similar business model in the lodging space. Lodging and computer services are very different industries with one similarity: there is a large fixed-asset component that is required to use it, even if the usage is for a short duration. For computer services, you need a data center loaded up with the latest servers, storage arrays, network, and security platforms. For lodging, you need real estate. Like computing platforms that are owned by large companies for their own use, the utilization is very low. This same situation occurs in vacation real estate that also often has very low utilization rates by the owners. Amazon solved the utilization issue in computer services by creating AWS. Airbnb (founded in 2008) solved the issue in lodging by creating a platform where people could monetize their spare capacity in their vacation real estate.

Like Amazon with AWS, Airbnb is a great example of a company that recognized an opportunity to connect people with residential space to rent with travelers interested in a lower cost or more homey location. Unlike Amazon's AWS, Airbnb doesn't actually own any property. It is a platform for property owners to monetize their own assets. And that platform was worth $35 billion as of 2019.

Airbnb is a Wave 3 company that pioneered the monetization of personal assets, such as real estate. It is a Wave 3 data-driven company.

Another example is Uber. Uber doesn't own any assets or have drivers as employees. Uber created a market to monetize the spare capacity of a driver's time and driving expertise, along with the spare capacity of their personal vehicle, and it sold taxi services to people who needed transportation. Uber didn't need a fleet of vehicles or a tremendous amount of capital to get started. Once it set up its platform, Uber was able to go global very quickly. Uber was founded in 2009 and followed a similar model to Amazon's AWS, except for the taxi business. Ten years after Uber was founded, it has almost $12 billion in revenue and a $75 billion market capitalization. It operates in 63 countries and 785 metropolitan areas. The company was renamed Uber Technologies, signaling that we can expect it to go into new markets and disrupt with the same playbook, such as Uber Eats, leveraging Uber to deliver prepared foods to people.

There are hundreds of similar Wave 3 upstarts too numerous to mention, looking to disrupt everything. What Wave 3 companies have going for them is that they don't care about the rules that industries have established and that old-school companies have been following. Startups come along and either don't know or don't care about the unspoken norms within the field, and they end up besting the old guard because of that freedom.

All of the Wave 3 companies represent demand-side threats to every company and industry sector that we can imagine. The resulting impact to white-collar workers in the companies that are being disrupted is not looking good. Just do the math. The successful Wave 3 companies simply employ fewer people to get the work done. Additionally, the profile of the people that they do hire would not be described as your typical white-collar workers.

Innovation and Riding the 3 Waves

Let's close out this chapter and talk about how innovation relates to riding the three Waves, versus getting washed out to sea.

Riding Wave 1. Riding Wave 1 is relatively straightforward. While there are certainly some creative aspects to executing a Wave 1 strategy, the key to success is more often about applying the existing market innovations that already exist into your environment. For Wave 1, you want to explore the innovations that already exist and apply them to your operations, instead of trying to innovate yourself.

Why? Because the operation of your business is not core to the strategic value of your firm. Do people buy Diet Coke because the Coca-Cola Company has an efficient or innovative data center operation? Do you buy an iPhone because Apple has an efficient process in its finance department? The answer is not only "no" in both cases, but the back office is almost irrelevant to these customer questions. The back-office operations need to be operationally effi-cient by reducing costs, improving quality, and workflow time. In other words, your back-office operation needs to be good enough so that it is efficient and not inhibiting your business model. To over-achieve in your back-office excel-lence (for example, by having the world's best custom financial platform) is a strategic blunder if that is not your core business. It consumes too much time, management attention, and capital. Your customers, or sources of revenue, do not care.

The second reason that you should not focus your innovation agenda on Wave 1 is that other businesses have innovated and are continuously inno-vating to provide more efficient services to support your operations. You are better off buying the innovation and services from the market instead of trying to re-invent the wheel. Many firms, whose sole purpose is to create efficient business services, are investing billions of dollars every year into innovation technologies and services. Focusing too much of your energy on Wave 1 by trying to outdo the market is a waste of time and money, and it distracts you from where the real money is: Waves 2 and 3.

Riding Waves 2 and 3. For your digital transformation to succeed in Waves 2 and 3, you MUST innovate from within. Why? Because impactful inno-vation for your firm requires very specific knowledge of your firm, your market, knowledge of the specific needs of your customers, and challenges to implement changes to the way the market is served (e.g., regulatory, legal, cultural, etc.).

You can buy innovation in Wave 1 and apply it to your Wave 1 transforma-tion plan. For Wave 2, you can buy only some of the ingredients for success, then you must innovate and create the rest of the ingredients for your market, your customers, in your industry, in order to have a successful Wave 2 trans-formation. For Wave 3, there is nothing to buy; it is all innovative creation, and, if done right, it will radically transform your business.

What's Next

In the next chapter, we will talk more about Wave 3 and the resulting implications on our business models, our labor markets, our politics, and our economy as a whole. The potential for driving tremendous Wave 3 value comes at a price of disrupting many entrenched interests. Those vested in the status quo will resist these changes that are coming. Those seeking to drive Wave 3 changes need to understand, in the broadest possible sense, the politics of change that comes with Wave 3.

CHAPTER 10:

The Business Implications of Future Tech

"Artificial intelligence is the future, not only for Russia,
but for all humankind ... It comes with colossal opportunities,
but also threats that are difficult to predict. Whoever becomes
the leader in this sphere will become the ruler of the world."

- Russian President Vladimir Putin in 2017

IS YOUR BUSINESS READY for Digital Labor? Or, asked another way, is your company willing to embrace the widespread changes that are coming? Because firms that are making an effort to accept and deal with technological advances will be far more successful than those choosing to ignore them. Companies that believe they can resist will be out of business in short order, because they won't be able to keep up. Legacy business models are hard to overcome.

The change that we're experiencing today is unlike any we've seen before. Most innovation is incremental, happening in stages, little by little. We've seen cell phones morph through several iterations from bulky handheld devices to palm-sized devices with the capability to take photos and video, play music and movies, provide navigation, and even track health metrics, among other things so far. Over several years, the smartphone has evolved.

What we're facing today will be nothing like the smartphone evolution. The change that is coming will not be incremental, despite what the experts keep assuring. The changes that are underway are massive. If you're not willing to change how you're doing business, it will be nearly impossible to benefit from the new models that emerge. And there will certainly be opportunity.

The Near-Term Business Value of AI

According to *Forbes*[23], Gartner estimates the business value of AI will hit $3.9 trillion by 2022, mainly by enhancing customer experience. Forty-four percent of that value will come from "decision support/augmentation" (i.e., supporting data science) says Gartner, with another 16 percent coming from "decision automation systems" (such as sending and receiving communiques via text, email, and voice). The remaining 40 percent of that value can't yet be determined, says Forbes' Alex Knapp. In other words, we know the impact will be big, but we can't yet envision what that impact will look like. As Knapp says, "The ability to process large datasets quickly, and the capability of processing that information in new and different ways, opens up a world of possibilities for new business that isn't imaginable today."

What Gartner is basically saying is that companies leveraging AI will benefit the most, because they will no longer need costly human labor, so their margins will increase along with their market share. Profits will rise, and business owners will become wealthier.

Another impact of this reduced reliance on human labor and AI advances is rising productivity. In its report, "AI to Drive GDP Gains of $15.7 trillion with Productivity, Personalization Improvements," PwC claims that AI will contribute $15.7 trillion to the gross domestic product (GDP) by 2030, half of which will come from labor productivity gains. To put that in perspective, the entire GDP in the US today is just over $19 trillion. Companies that are implementing advanced technology, such as AI, will be among the first to benefit from these productivity gains, and businesses that insist on sticking to old processes and technology will not. They won't survive long term.

Not only will AI allow companies to do what humans formerly did better, faster, and cheaper, so companies can do more in less time, but AI also enables organizations to do things they previously couldn't. However, those that adopt advanced technology can gain a head start in innovation that will be nearly impossible to beat.

Digital markets have a tendency to be winner-take-all due the nature of digital products and services. Digital products and services can scale usually without limit and are not bound by geography, time of day, capital, or other constraints typical in classic analog markets. The best restaurant in New York City will not have an effect on restaurants in San Francisco. However, a digital book, like this one, can be downloaded an infinite number of times across a variety of platforms without any incremental or marginal cost to the publisher.

Google Maps is another prime example. Garmin and TomTom used to be competitors in the auto navigation market; today, they're barely in the game because there is no marginal cost to Google for making its maps and navigation ubiquitous. In fact, Google makes them free and gets money on the back end from advertising and content tie-ins. In digital markets, second and third place are often a very distant second or third to the market leader.

The Evolution of AI

Just as AI is triggering an evolution of business models, AI itself has evolved. It started as a narrowly focused technology, designed to complete a very specific task. For example, you could replace a customer service rep with an AI chat bot, because the scope of what the AI needed to do to be effective was quite narrow. Or remember Google Duplex and its ability to act as a concierge of sorts, setting up hair-cutting appointments or making restaurant reservations? It could act in your place, but only within a very limited window. It could get you a seat at your local Italian restaurant, but it couldn't pick out seats to tomorrow's baseball game, because it was only engineered to that narrow spectrum of restaurant reservations.

Narrow AI is very good at what it was programmed to do, whether that's playing the game Fortnite or turning on your coffee maker every morning at 5:30 a.m. It may win at Fortnite every time but fail at playing other games like Mario Kart or Halo, just as it can't turn on the washing machine or dryer automatically, despite being able to control the coffee maker. Narrow AI is like a smart machine, and it's typically better than a human at its very focused task.

General AI, however, is much broader: it mimics human intelligence. It goes deep in a few areas but broad in all areas, much like human learning. General AI has the ability to understand and learn. General AI can also apply narrow intelligence to other similar situations. For example, it could take the narrow ability to control the coffee machine and figure out how to control other devices that have similar interfaces and control mechanisms. General AI learns from the experience and can teach itself new applications. Think of General AI as narrow AI with broad capabilities. General AI is years away, likely in the latter half of the 2020s.

Super AI (or super intelligence) is where AI is both broad and deep in all areas, well beyond human intelligence. We're a decade or more away from this capability, as of 2019. But as soon as machines acquire sentience or become aware, they will very quickly become super intelligent as they will teach themselves at machine speed. Super intelligence will emerge shortly after general intelligence is reached.

What people seem to misunderstand about AI is that we are quickly approaching a point at which we won't be able to stop its march toward super intelligence. We can't just turn it off or set some ground rules. Narrow AI, which has strict boundaries, isn't so scary to people; when it works well, it makes our lives easier.

What should be scary is when the system starts to operate in its own self-interest. And when that point comes, we will be unable to stop its further development because it will have designed ways to ensure you can't unplug it. Its goals and morals will likely be entirely different from our own, and it will be something we won't be able to control. That time is quickly approaching.

Many people—even people who are tech savvy—do not appreciate this notion of machines becoming out of our control. It is a certainty that it will happen—it is math. *When* it will happen is debatable. If you have doubts, I highly encourage you to watch Sam Harris's Ted talk on this subject, entitled, "Can we build AI without losing control over it?"

The Biggest Forces Pushing this Exponential Advancement

AI will evolve to super intelligence through deep learning, artificial neural networks, generative adversarial networks (GANs), quantum computing, swarm AI, and other cognitive technologies.

Deep Learning. Deep learning uses artificial neural networks that are self-coded, or self-taught, by the machines. These artificial neural networks can recognize complex patterns in large data sets and teach themselves based on those patterns.

This type of machine learning is different from derivative or rules-based learning. In rules-based learning, you apply a set of rules, such as " ... if that, then this ... " to determine the answer. Machine learning starts with inputs and outputs and derives the rules based on pattern matching.

Google Translate originally used rules-based translations, but that was problematic when you had two languages with very different sentence structures, such as Chinese and English. When you translate using a derivative model, it's not quite correct. It's not as evident when you're translating two Latin-based languages, but when you move to Eastern languages, it's very difficult to find parallel words and phrases.

In early 2017, Google moved to machine learning, which it called Google Neural Machine Translation (GNMT). GNMT looked at millions of translations that were already in the archives and "learned" the language by observations. This learning was encoded in GNMT's artificial neural networks, and its foreign language translations have improved markedly in the past few years.

This type of learning is how computers beat the world's chess champion and GO champion as well. The machines taught themselves how to play better than humans.

It's also how software is getting better at healthcare diagnoses than some doctors. Today, the technology exists for you to use your smartphone to take a close-up photo of a suspicious mole and upload it to an app that checks for skin cancer. However, regulations place limits on this type of technology deployment because it is not credentialed, as a doctor is. State and federal medical regulators will have to reconcile this new technology into their old medical delivery models.

The technologies behind deep learning, like artificial neural networks, generative adversarial networks (GANs), unsupervised machine learning, and others do not encode their logic in simple to review rule sets. The logic is typically encoded in a hidden layer of the neural framework. Essentially, a black box that makes it difficult to deconstruct into an "if that, then this" type of rule set. Risk management, compliance, regulatory, and legal systems will have to get comfortable with the overall effectiveness of any deep learning system before there is widespread adoption. For example, if human errors in a process can be reduced by 95 percent or more, then deep learning systems will have likely proved their effectiveness and "manual" or human based operations may even become prohibited. If driverless cars become widely accepted and have a far superior safety record than human drivers, how long will it take to prohibit human drivers from the system?

Quantum Computing. Quantum computing is another force that will drive AI advancement. In computer science, most computers are two-state systems—i.e., binary—consisting of ones or zeros. Quantum computing leverages the properties of quantum mechanics and expands the limitations of a binary states.

Quantum computing is still in the research and development phase, and it's very complicated, but when Quantum computing becomes ready for broad commercial use, it will be exponentially more powerful that today's computing platforms. Currently (at the time of this writing), there are half a dozen companies experimenting with quantum computing, with the promise of being able to process very complex data sets at very quickly. Today's supercomputers either take too long or simply cannot process this level of complexity and scale.

As quantum computing takes computing to the next level, it will enable us to do such things as render mixed reality, augmented reality in real time, especially when you combine it with 5G networks. You will be able to use your smartphone as a processing hub to leverage very powerful edge computing on the phone and quantum-enabled cloud processing.

Swarm AI. Swarm AI is another force impacting our future. Swarm AI uses our understanding of biological systems to inform how we design some AI platforms. Think of an ant colony, where the life form is the colony, rather than the ant. The way the colony operates is that an ant on one side of the colony may not be aware of what an ant on the other side of the colony is doing, but they are both connected to the colony, along with all of the other ants. They are working together very efficiently.

The same is true with bee colonies and fish swarms. These natural systems in biology with decentralized communication and decision making are now being used in Swarm AI to create hybrid systems to resolve problems. In 2016, a firm called Unanimous AI used Swarm AI to predict the outcome of the first four places in the Kentucky Derby—the elusive Superfecta bet, where a $1 bet paid $541.10.

There are many more examples of innovation on the exponential forces driving AI. When people ask me what's going to happen in the next five or ten years, I have to admit that I don't know. No one can yet conceive of what it's going to look like. But it's going to look so different from today that many of today's investments and strategies will be obsolete in short order.

Future AI Scenarios: Utopian and Dystopian

There are a number of arguments about what our future will look like. Some experts, such as Peter Diamandis (who we discussed in Chapter 8), paint a picture of a utopia. He argues that technology will create more abundance and that the poorest among us will benefit the most. In contrast, the pessimists describe a dystopia. What's most likely is actually a tale of two cities, with wealth concentration at the top and rising unemployment at the bottom.

In the US, we're already experiencing utopia. Americans live in a world of abundance where the poorest among us live as royalty did 200 years ago. Even the poorest in the US have access to smartphones, running water, relative safety, good medical care, indoor plumbing. Even poor citizens aren't dying of obscure diseases, as they did 200 or 300 years ago. The things we take for granted in modern life used to be luxuries, or simply unavailable to anyone.

Usually, when we think of abundance, we imagine the examples of the uber-wealthy, such as yachts, jets, and mansions. But basic abundance is more pervasive than uber wealth. In the US, food is abundant, clothes are abundant, shelter is abundant, entertainment options are abundant. The abundance we enjoy makes basic survival (such as food, shelter, clothing, safety, etc.) relatively easy for most people. These are the two lowest levels of Maslow's hierarchy, shown below. Largely, it has been technological advances that have led to abundance at the base levels of Maslow's hierarchy.

Technology is to thank for this relative abundance in our lives today. The issue is: will it continue? Or will future abundance be less democratic or less distributed to most of our society? If abundance recedes from large portions of the population, we start looking at some dystopian outcomes, at least for some.

Future dystopian scenarios usually are derived from the fact that large portions of the population are left behind as society and technology progresses. This is a real risk for many white-collar workers who ignore the trends and do not try to adapt to the technological advances that are coming; we'll see massive unemployment. Adaptation doesn't mean trying to compete with

Maslow's Hierarchy of Needs

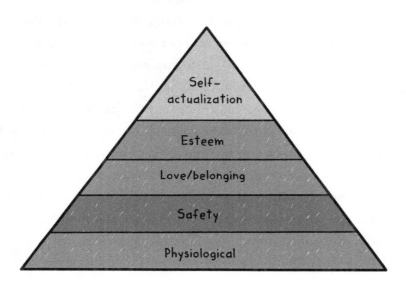

the machines and AI, because we're biological creatures and we can't compete with machine speed. We just can't. But we can adapt.

Ideally, we would build safeguards into the systems to ensure that the types of change and pace and the nature of change are aligned with our societal ability to adapt. We do this today with advancements in drugs. However, safeguards can slow down the pace of adoption and increase the costs, but they are designed to protect the public in the case of drug development.

However, applying safeguards to AI will be viewed by the priests of innovation as sacrilege. This was the lesson in the movie *Jurassic Park,* where the dinosaurs ran amok after control was lost. Jeff Goldblum utters a line in the movie: "Your scientists were so preoccupied with whether or not they could, they didn't stop to think if they should."

In March 2017, at the SXSW festival in Austin, TX, one of the apostles of technology innovation, Elon Musk, argued for putting safeguards in place for AI. He said, "AI is the rare case where I think we need to be proactive in regulation instead of reactive. Because I think by the time we are reactive in AI regulation, it'll be too late. AI is a fundamental risk to the existence of human civilization." Wow. Was that a sensational line to get attention? Probably, but is it true? Maybe. It depends on how AI rolls out.

As much as it may be prudent to tread carefully with the AI innovation, there are two roads we could go down with respect to future safeguards. One way is the safe way, which requires setting up restrictions and safeguards to limit the uncontrolled progression of technologies. The other way is full support for technology development without any safeguards at all. That's the easier road and, realistically, someone is going to choose it. So even if all the countries in the world agree to implement safeguards, if even one goes rogue, then there will be no way to walk back safeguards later.

One of the problems of the absence of safeguards is the lack of discernment possible with AI. If you program the AI to eliminate all unwanted telemarketing calls, it may achieve this goal by eliminating phones. No phones, no unwanted phone calls. OK, then add the constraint that you cannot get rid of phones, and the AI decides to eliminate electricity from the planet. No electricity, the phones don't work, no unwanted calls. You can see where this is going. So, safeguards are crucial in a sense, but who will write them, and will we all agree on the constraints or safeguards?

AI innovators have to be very careful when creating optimization algorithms to be clear about what the AI is trying to optimize. Is it money? Value? Human life?

In Sam Harris' Ted Talk, he makes the argument that it's not a question of *if* there will be a bad outcome; it's a question of *when*. AI is extremely powerful, and the nation that can control it will become the dominant force. Regulation now is the only way to even the playing field and protect the dangerous changes that could come.

Rather than a utopian or dystopian view, there is the view that the future will consist of the very wealthy and the very poor—a tale of two cities. We're already starting to see this in the US, with the wealth concentration at the top becoming more pronounced. The middle class is already disappearing but will do so more quickly and dramatically in some scenarios. The impact at the bottom hasn't been fully realized yet, however. But with technology progression, the divide will become very clear very quickly. If you adapt and end up on the on the right side of change, you'll thrive, and if you're on the wrong side, you'll struggle.

Ethics and Social Implications of Regulating AI

Keeping in mind the example of eliminating unwanted telemarketing calls described earlier, let's talk about how we might regulate AI. What is the cost to us of waiting to regulate? Is it even possible to regulate AI?

One possible way to curb AI is to use separate AI control systems that are smart enough to keep up with the advancing systems. While this is theoretically possible, it is very difficult to achieve and would likely be a temporary measure. Additionally, it would require all developers of AI to design their systems with this in mind—again, not likely.

Really, the only way to curb AI's progression is by regulating adoption, which I think we'll see with such products as the driverless car, for example. With so many jobs potentially being eliminated when driverless cars become the standard, it's likely there will be a political reaction to clamp down on production of these autonomous cars.

There are also ethical issues with the application of AI under certain circumstances. Sticking with the driverless car example, humans have different value systems across different cultures and countries. An AI's value system is what—that of its creator? Of its underlying data set that it was trained on? Something else?

All societies value human life; however, in situations where choices need to be made, whose life do we value the most? It is a numbers game? If so, what numbers? Headcount, FICO scores, social scores from Facebook, etc.?

Think through an example with the driverless car, when the situation evolves and the car has to make a choice between hitting a mother and her baby and hitting a crowd of people. Most drivers will not see the crowd on the sidewalk and swerve to miss the mother and child in the road. They may, in fact, injure many more people as a result, but, societally, we accept that as an unfortunate accident. The driver could not have processed all of the scenarios and reacted to avoid hitting the mother and child suddenly popping out on the road.

How will we react when the driverless car is in the same situation? When something goes awry, the car may use facial recognition software to identify everyone in the vicinity. The driverless car theoretically sees the mother and baby *and* sees the crowd and can make a value-based decision as to the ideal action to take. Perhaps the AI chooses to scan everyone's identity and sees that one person has just three months to live, so maybe they steer the car in their direction. This is a very slippery slope: should the car save the mom and child and hit the crowd, or hit the mother and baby and save the crowd?

Should facial recognition and FICO scores be considered in the calculation? It may sound crazy but constraining the calculation and optimization algorithm is essentially regulation. Should the car manufacturer optimize the algorithm to minimize lawsuits? Should the algorithm be optimized to maximize safety for the driver and passengers? Should regulators optimize around certain classes of people?

The whole decision matrix brings up the issue of ethics and who gets to decide how AI evaluates such situations. Who is the priority? What factors should be considered when choosing who lives and who dies? Should we make it better for the driver, better for the car, better for society? Because the interests of each are very different and often in conflict, it makes the job of regulating very difficult. Beyond difficult, it takes time to think this through as a society. The technology is progressing rapidly with or without the consideration.

So who gets to decide? Who is the regulator?

Right now, I think the only way to approach the larger ethical issues surrounding AI would be to put the burden on companies to explain the goal set—that is, what they are trying to achieve—and the programming constraints and implications before going into production with the technology. We can't quantify human values and morality, to establish metrics for decisions, and even if we could, some societies have different values. Does the society value youth over age? Are certain classes of people more valued than others? There's a conflict that needs to be resolved, at least on a country-by-country basis. These are broad generalizations, and even within societies, there is no universal agreement.

What it comes down to is the need for disclosure and transparency. Disclosure is about being open and truthful about what is being optimized and the risks and rewards of advancing technology. This allows humans to develop their own strategies for dealing with any heightened risk to their interests associated with AI. For example, if it were discovered that driverless cars were more likely to hit pedestrians than other cars, and that it avoided anything that is yellow, it is probable that we would see many more people wearing yellow on their walk to work or school, as a defense mechanism.

Transparency is a related concept and argues for not holding back information from oversight from the public.

The problem we will likely face with unregulated AI is that its values will likely not be aligned with our own. Then, at some point in the future, the AI will become self-aware or sentient and it will have its own goal set and set its own parameters. But it won't have emotions or morals; in fact, it will have no emotion, only a focus on goal attainment. And if humans get in the way of its goals, they will be viewed as an obstacle to the goal and could be dealt with or removed from the picture.

Just as we don't go after ants that are crawling around on the ground—we won't attack them—but we also won't try and avoid stepping on them if they're in our path, AI is very likely to view humans in the same vein. That is, humans who interfere with them reaching their goal will be in peril. You may be thinking that we can encode a human moral fabric into all AI, but that belief is based in hope, not reality. How would you do it? Who would do it? When? Would it even work? If you haven't watched the Sam Harris Ted Talk referenced earlier, now would be a good time.

The Business Implications of Digital Labor

Let's shift to the more practical realities of the short- to medium-term business implications of Digital Labor and AI. Whether your business is ready for Digital Labor depends a lot on your understanding of your culture, your capabilities, and your competitive landscape.

Your Organization's Culture. Within your corporate culture, how does your organization deal with technology advancements? Is your organization resistant to change or does it embrace change? Is tried-and-true the norm, or is innovation and risk-taking celebrated? You need to understand your culture in order to achieve transformative innovation.

Your culture also affects how your business is perceived by your customer base. Do people in your business have a high interaction with the public, such as in retail stores? Or is it mostly back-office, as with Facebook? If you do not factor in the human reaction of your employees to the changes that are coming, you will not be able to craft the most effective transformation agenda.

Your Company's Capabilities. Understanding your capabilities is another aspect of success. Today's technology requires a lot of new talent and capabilities. Recruiting this type of risk-taking talent is a specific skillset that most firms today don't have, largely because the talent is scarce and expensive. The ideal workers of tomorrow need to be multi-disciplined (polymaths), in order to pull together comprehensive transformative solutions in your business. It is important to get expert help to give you a roadmap to avoid making the same mistakes others have made.

There are two types of help firms need today. One is an explorer capable of breaking new ground or creating a new path. That's the bleeding edge of change. As we mentioned in Chapter 8, the other type of help companies need is the jungle guide (instead of an explorer) who leads people through unchartered territory and shows them how to do things few people have done before. Once the road has been paved, organizations can largely figure the way out themselves, but we're not yet at that point. Right now, we're still in the jungle looking for a path. And few organizations have the resident capabilities to blaze a trail through on their own.

Your Company's Competitors. The last aspect that determines if your company is ready is understanding your competitive landscape. Technology is advancing so quickly that no organization is immune to disruption, despite the fact that it may not be obvious. Change may sneak up on you. As shown in the graph below, at first an exponential trend can appear to be linear, until the "elbow" of the curve is reached. At that point, the y-axis variable starts to increase rapidly, where x is time and y is technology growth or capability. In terms of digital enterprise technologies, we are somewhere around the elbow, as the instantaneous nature of digital tools pushes this trend forward.

Exponential vs Linear Growth

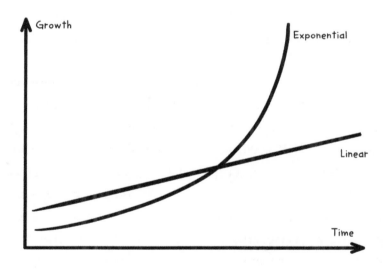

Even if you are concerned your company isn't ready to forge ahead with advanced technology, if the competitive landscape is indicating you're going to fall behind, you need to act now, no matter what. In such a circumstance, almost any action is better than no action. Because if you do nothing, your competition will gain such an advantage from which you'll never recover.

Also remember (from Chapter 9) that there are two kinds of competition: direct competitors on the supply side and indirect competitors on the demand side. The competitors on the supply side are ventures that do what your company does but better, faster, cheaper. You know who they are. Where businesses tend to get blindsided is on the demand side, where firms use advanced technologies to solve your customers' problems in a way that undermines your market. The nature of exponential change and the lowering of barriers to participation in digital delivery models can allow competition to emerge from several directions you're probably not expecting.

What Businesses Need to Do to Be Successful

To take advantage of the coming opportunities that advanced technology will provide, while protecting against demand-side market shifts, businesses need to focus on talent, technology, and processes. These are three things that are critical for companies to start addressing in order to be successful in the future.

Hire the Right Talent. Talent is the first challenge, because acquiring expertise and developing it are two things that many businesses struggle with. On the acquisition side, the cost to retain experts is high. For example, you might pay an engineer $85,000, but an engineer who is a cybersecurity expert may demand $225,000—almost triple what the generalist is being paid.

Some people on your team will balk and question whether such a premium is necessary, or even fair to the generalist engineer. The answer is yes, if you need a cybersecurity expert, you'll need to pay what the market demands. And the people on your team who are questioning the salary continuum need to come to grips with the fact that good talent is expensive. Not having it is even more expensive.

Sports franchises aren't bound by these restrictions: the All-Star point guard makes more than the coach, and the coach makes more than the general manager, despite the fact that the hierarchy is flipped when it comes to decision-making power. Yet that's what is needed for basketball teams to win championships, and that's what businesses need to get comfortable doing in order to be competitive.

Looking ahead, I think we are going to see more meritocracy-based systems and compensation models that are very different from paying salaries. That means considering renting expertise as you need it, rather than buying it. Renting an expert means retaining an expert to deal with a particular challenge or project, rather than on an ongoing basis as an employee.

Lawyers and accountants work this way already: you pay them on a project or hourly basis to advise you or review your financials, but you don't have to hire them as full-time employees. To be competitive going forward, organizations need to begin retaining the expertise they need, as they need it, much like they pay for professional services.

Identify the Technologies You Need. After expertise and human resources, next, businesses need to create a technology roadmap. When my firm, Rumjog, works with clients, we assess where the client organization is today and what its desired state is, and then we map out what it's going to take to get to that desired future state. Of course, with technology being so adaptive and ever-changing, that roadmap is never cast in stone; it has to be flexible and constantly updated along the way. But you need to be honest with yourselves about your current capabilities and what it's going to take technology-wise to shore up those capabilities.

Most organizations want to know where to go with AI, automation, and Digital Labor. At the heart of readiness for these technologies is the firm's data strategy. Being AI-ready is about more than just data; it requires having the proper frameworks in place for data and enterprise architectures to drive the AI technologies and Digital Labor into the market. It is crucial to develop a technology roadmap, especially if you're handcuffed to a legacy platform and need to find a way to break free in order to achieve your long-term goals.

Develop Your Business Processes. The last dimension is the business model and business case, where it's important to try many approaches and not get married to one outcome. It's better to try and fail fast than to stick with a path that isn't working. Just keep trying.

There are new business models to embrace, and companies need to have a growth mindset up front. In this sense, your business case needs to have both offensive and defensive components. Offensive strategies involve exploiting digital data exhaust to identify new business opportunities, or even entirely new business models. Offense is about the strategic application of new technologies and insights to create revenue opportunities in new ways. Trying defensive strategies, which focus on doing things better, faster, cheaper, won't have the same business impact as an offensive strategy, but they are enablers of an aggressive offensive strategy. Whereas offense is the exploitation of data and insights, defense is the master data management, data hygiene, and rethinking data ownership to make possible the offensive work.

It's important to break down the amount of benefits realized into two dimensions: defense and offense. Most companies think about Digital Labor as automation and as the gateway to saving money, reducing labor costs, replacing people with software that runs 24/7 without fail. And those companies are right in one sense. You do have to get the defensive playbook right.

However, your business case strategy is incomplete without thinking about your offensive capabilities. What is your business able to do that it wasn't capable of before? Take Amazon, again. Amazon has been very successful at selling products better, faster, and cheaper. It uses Amazon Prime to compensate for shipping that isn't overnight or isn't as fast as other retailers can be. However, the one thing Amazon can do better than other retailers is carrying 50 times the inventory and product selection and staying open 24/7/365. It never closes, which opens up the potential for business in all other markets; it can serve a global market, not only its local zip code.

The truth is, most people and businesses are simply not fully ready for the changes that are coming, so the more you can do to prepare, the better off you and your organization will be.

But the first thing we need to do is start having more conversations about AI and our future.

CHAPTER 11:

Digital Labor and the Impact on the Human Condition

"The purpose of life is to contribute in some way to making things better."
– Robert F. Kennedy

IN EARLIER CHAPTERS, we discussed how the coming progressions of Digital Labor will have a significant and accelerating impact on white-collar jobs. Just as many routine physical jobs (often referred to as blue-collar jobs) were replaced by physical machines over the last few decades, advances in software and platforms will replace the more cerebral jobs that largely define the white-collar worker set.

In the absence of an articulated vision for what the future will hold, people tend to gravitate to dystopian points of view because the unknown, or the new future, is scary. If white-collar jobs get replaced with software, what happens to me? What happens to my family and friends? What happens to my community, and society as a whole? These are profound questions and, rather than pontificate one vision of the future over another, this chapter breaks down these questions and offers some elements to give you confidence that you can steer your life in a positive direction.

In the previous chapter, we alluded to Charles Dickens's *A Tale of Two Cities*, a fictional tome that took place in Paris during the French Revolution.

The opening sentence in the book is:

> "It was the best of times, it was the worst of times, it was the age of wisdom, it was the age of foolishness, it was the epoch of belief, it was the epoch of incredulity, it was the season of Light, it was the season of Darkness, it was the spring of hope, it was the winter of despair, we had everything before us, we had nothing before us, we were all going direct to Heaven, we were all going direct the other way—in short, the period was so far like the present period, that some of its noisiest authorities insisted on its being received, for good or for evil, in the superlative degree of comparison only."

This sentence will likely come to define the coming age. There will be winners and losers. There will be believers and disbelievers. There will be hope and despair.

However, our allusion breaks with Dickens on a key fundamental point. In the coming age, defined by a post-Digital Labor revolution, you will have a choice on which of the two cities to live in. White-collar workers who fail to understand the choices to be made and who ignore the warnings in this book are more likely to experience the worst of times. On the other hand, if you make the right choices, it could be the best of times.

How Time Affects Your Life's Purpose

If you go to a party today and introduce yourself to someone new, invariably one of the first questions you will be asked is, "What do you do?" In our culture, we tend to define people based on their vocation, rather than who they really are. We tend to do this because work, or a job, takes up the majority of our time during our adult life.

But are we really the sum total of the work that we do? I hope not. Gallup runs worldwide polling on job engagement in the workplace. In June 2017, on the Gallup chairman's blog[24], the company reported that only 15 percent of workers are engaged in their jobs—which means that across the world, 85 percent of workers are not engaged. Google the article if you are interested in the details but, suffice it to say, there seems to be an identity issue here. If our culture defines "you" based on what job you have, and most people are not engaged in their jobs, can this really be who we are? No, it cannot.

At the heart of the issue for people to consider here is this: in the post-Digital Labor markets, you need to align who you are, your purpose, and your work. That may sound lofty and somewhat touchy feely; nonetheless, you will not succeed in tomorrow's markets if you do not like working. Do not confuse a job with working—they are not the same thing. Philosophically, think of working as contributing to the world around you, and think of having a job as selling your time to do what you are told. When you frame it that way, no wonder 85 percent of people are not engaged in their jobs.

The opening quote of this chapter by Bobby Kennedy gets at the heart of life's purpose. But everyone is different, with different passions, interests, talents, and situations. A useful exercise to get a sense of future purpose is to consider the notion of time.

What would you do if you had more time? In your professional life, what would you do if you could complete the work assigned to your job in half the time it takes you today? What would you do? Could you contribute towards achieving higher goals for the organization? Or do you have the perspective that you would be half as valuable as an employee of the firm?

In your personal life, what would your day look like if you had hours to spend on personal pursuits? How would you choose to use your time if your work day were far shorter than it is today? Many people today are unable to answer this simple question, beyond the trite responses. Saying that you would travel or relax are short-term things to do that recognize that you are likely tired. Saying you would travel or relax is not a long-term answer to the question, because without a purpose, eventually you will become miserable relaxing and traveling.

Think about how to answer the time question if it is reworded like this:
If I had had the time, how could I align my skills, my passions, and my interests to benefit those around me?

This question applies to both your personal and professional life. In the ideal, the distinction between personal and professional gets lost. If you could spend your time leveraging the things that you like to do, that you are passionate about, that you have the skills for, you would never have to work again.

Most people's reaction to this way of thinking is to dismiss it because of the practicalities of needing to make money to support oneself and family—to pay the bills. That is the wrong way to think about it. This is a thought exercise to help you move in a direction that will allow you to succeed in the coming age. By moving in a direction, it suggests taking steps toward a new way, not quitting your job and abandoning what you are doing today. Just understand this: change is coming and your job, whatever it is, is going to change dramatically in the next 5 to 10 years. By thinking along the lines of time and purpose now, you can put yourself in the driver's seat to take control of the change, instead of being a victim of change.

A Practical Approach to Considering Time and Your Life's Purpose

The unconstrained approach to answering the time-and-purpose question is useful for identifying the areas that you are passionate about. If these passions are relevant to the marketplace, then this allows you to have fun and get paid, instead of going to work every Monday morning and looking forward to the next weekend. Not all passions are practical pursuits in the post-Digital Labor markets. By reading to this point in the book, it is a safe bet that you have some interest in the emerging technologies that are driving Digital Labor. Having a passion for technology is, for the most part, a necessity, but it's not the only ingredient to future success. The exciting thing is to combine the knowledge of the technical trends to other non-technical areas to drive understanding on changes in a particular field.

For example, let's say your passion is golf. How will emerging technology impact the game of golf and, more important, the business of golf? Such technologies as RFID ball trackers, shot tracers, virtual reality, and drone flyovers of golf course layouts will all have an impact. Two brothers in the

UK, Steve and Dave Jolliffe, had a passion for golf and an understanding of the technology that could impact the game of golf. They also saw some of the problems with golf, such as the amount of time it took to play, the real estate footprint, and the boring driving ranges.

In 2000, they formed TopGolf, which took technology and married it to the driving range, and their business took off. The driving range balls are fed to you individually and encoded with RFID tracer chips. You hit the balls to various targets and score points based on whatever game you choose. Like bowling, it is highly social, with automated scoring and food and drink being served. More than half the people who play at TopGolf are not traditional golfers (i.e., people who typically play 18 holes on the weekend).

TopGolf has more than 55 locations, generating $20 to $25 million per facility—a $1 billion operation. When the brothers Joliffe started TopGolf, they were not working in the classic sense of the word. Instead, they were pursuing a passion. In that sense, it was fun.

Let's look at another example. Say your passion is women's fashion. It's hard to think how emerging technology would impact that, but that is exactly what Jennifer Hyman and Jennifer Fleiss did in 2009 when they formed Rent the Runway. As we mentioned briefly in Chapter 9, Rent the Runway is an online service that provides designer outfits and accessories on a rental basis. It is very similar to the early Netflix model, where you rented DVDs through the mail, except instead of a DVD, you can rent a Louis Vuitton dress and handbag, for example. Women pay a monthly subscription and can borrow designer garments and accessories, which are delivered to your home and returned the same way. Ten years after Rent the Runway was formed, it is valued at $1 billion.

When you think of golf and women's fashion, it is unlikely that you think about emerging technology. That is the point of these examples. They explore how our passions can be combined with new thinking from a technology perspective to invent whole new business models and opportunities. They create new ways to contribute and impact our society. Not every idea is a good one. In fact, most are not, but that does not mean that you should not explore them if you have a passion for it and if your motivation is to make an impact.

As we look across the landscape of white-collar workers, every single field in every single industry is going to be impacted by Digital Labor. "Work in America," written Carl E. Van Horn and Herbert A. Schaffner describes white-collar workers as follows:

"A white-collar worker is a person who performs professional, managerial, or administrative work. White-collar work may be performed in an office or other administrative setting. White-collar includes business management, customer support, market research, finance, engineering, operations research, marketing, information technology, networking, attorneys, medical professional, public relation, talent professionals, architects, graphic design, stockbrokers, accounting, auditor, actuary, customs professional, research and development and contracting."

Each one of these functional jobs, in literally every industry sector, will be impacted in the next few years. You can go through many examples of picking a job class from the list—for example, finance professional. Then pick a sector—say, health care—and think through how technology will impact these jobs. Finance professionals will go through a tremendous change in the next 5 to 10 years, and the opportunities to be part of that change are abundant. Technologies such as blockchain, mobile computing, big data, and machine learning will change the way work gets done. Further knowledge about regulation for data privacy (HIPPA) and use will inhibit some solutions and enable others.

If you are a finance professional in health care, your future lies in understanding how these technology forces can be organized to transform the way finance work gets done in health care. The focus on a positive impact to society, such as eliminating fraud or providing transparency of costs, will drive the passion to pursue, if this is your interest.

This exercise can and should be done in every area of white-collar work, by the white-collar workers themselves—the very people who are likely to be impacted by Digital Labor. They know first and foremost where the positive potential impacts can be made. The paradigm needs to be making an impact instead of merely preserving a job. If you make an impact, your job prospects will be abundant. If you try to preserve your job, you will likely get washed under by the tide of change coming. Like the child who builds a sand castle at low tide and builds a moat to protect the castle from the incursion of the rising waves, this strategy works temporarily, and then it does not.

Jobs in the Wake of Digital Labor

Digital Labor transformations will not only change the number of white-collar workers required to support businesses and business functions, but the nature and structure of the remaining jobs, as well as new jobs, will change from the current form. Generally speaking, Digital Labor will replace a portion of classic human jobs, not the entire 40-hour work week. When that happens, we are left with fractional jobs—essentially a job can get done in less than a full-time, 40-hour work week. People will tend to fill this spare capacity with other things. Most of the time, they fill it with busy work, rather than work that is of higher value to the organization. This is one of the early obstacles to Digital Labor deployments: it is difficult to find the labor savings from the automation of work. However, this is only a temporary obstacle that will be overcome.

One way that businesses can prevent employees from filling up their time with non-value-added busy work is to break down jobs into smaller tasks or components. Jobs are then recast to the delivery of outputs, instead of the organization using a time-based measure.

What does this mean? Think of getting paid for how much work you've completed, rather than how many hours you spent doing that work. In the industrial age, this was called piecework. In the service economy, such projects are called gigs. Given how Digital Labor is progressing, the remaining work that is not impacted by Digital Labor is called residual labor. As seen in the graphic below, as Digital Labor does more and more of the classical job components, the residual labor shrinks in quantity *and* the nature of residual labor becomes expert. Think of it as expert concentration.

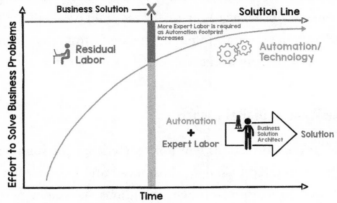

This residual expert labor typically does not lend itself to a classic Monday-through-Friday, 9-to-5 job. The residual expertise is required when the Digital Labor is not working, and it is episodic or random in nature. This episodic structure is perfect for the gig economy.

Let's look at a simple straightforward example—Uber drivers. As we've described throughout this book, the bulk of Uber's business is run by digital platforms: the customer interface, the dispatch and driver-rider matching systems, the mapping and routing, the pricing, the billing and collections, and other functions. However, until Uber figures out how to deploy the driverless Uber car, it still needs drivers. These drivers are not needed Monday through Friday from 9-to-5, however; instead, drivers are needed when and where people need rides. That changes—it is episodic and random. Uber does not hire drivers, it pays for gigs or completed rides. Drivers are not paid by the hour, they are paid a portion of the cost of the ride.

This is a familiar example of how expert residual labor will be acquired by companies in the future. However, in order to purchase labor from the market this way, two primary conditions need to be met. The first is that you need to re-organize the work into definable elements or containers with an objective output. That's easier said than done, but it's not impossible. The second condition is that you need a marketplace to procure this expert labor in the form of a gig. This is where crowdsourcing platforms emerge on the scene.

The Emergence of Crowdsourcing

What is crowdsourcing? Think of it as sourcing labor from the crowd, instead of from an employee. There are many crowdsourcing platforms on the scene today and many more being built to cover everything from routine micro-tasks to complex work, such as data science problems.

One example of crowdsourcing is Amazon's Mechanical Turk platform (which we first mentioned in Chapter 5). Amazon's platform sets up micro-tasks to be performed for a small fee. Most of the fees for micro-tasks range from $0.01/task to $1/task. A company using OCR (optical character recognition) to scan receipts for expense reports will have some portion that gets kicked out of the system because the OCR scan does not match the image. A firm could pay $0.05/image to validate the handwritten number on a receipt. This is much more cost-effective and fast compared to using employees or contractors to perform the same work.

Another crowdsourcing example is Fiverr. Fiverr was originally a platform of small tasks that people would do for $5—from simple graphics design (such as building a new logo), to voice work, to writing, and even marketing. The jobs start at $5 and go up from there. Spend a few dollars and try out this site. At Rumjog, we use Fiverr for a lot of projects: voice narration for podcasts, logo design, writing, PowerPoint graphics, even small programming jobs. In fact, all of the graphics in this book were made for $5 each.

Not all of the crowdsourcing projects are small, straightforward micro-tasks. In Chapter 4, we discussed Wipro's TopCoder platform, which performs enterprise application design and development, data science and analytics, mobile app development, and more. Topcoder has more than 1 million workers who compete for work in a winner-take-all model. Prizes range from a few hundred dollars to $25,000 and more. Customers of TopCoder will present a challenge and desired outcome, and the TopCoder community will compete to complete the challenge. Customers choose the winner based on which team or person submitted the best outcome for the challenge.

Let's say you want an iPhone app for a special event. You lay out what you are looking for with the constraints and set the prize pool, for example, $10,000. In 1 to 2 weeks, you'll receive several completed designs to choose from at a cost of $10,000. At Rumjog, we have used TopCoder and other crowdsourcing platforms for projects like this. It is less expensive and work is done in days, instead of weeks or months.

Each of these three examples has a slightly different business model to organize around the crowdsourcing idea:

1. Micro-task and fee defined—workers conform to the work (e.g., Mechanical Turk)
2. Project or gig and fee defined—buyers conform (e.g., Fiverr)
3. Work/output setup as competition— (e.g., TopCoder)

The challenge for all crowdsourcing platforms is to find a way to appropriately package the outputs needed into small definable buckets of work. The work or the output must be easily understood and structured, and that is not always easy.

As Digital Labor progresses in the economy, more and more residual labor (or specialized expert labor) will move to crowdsourcing platforms, allowing talent to be bought and sold online. At TopCoder, most (90 percent) of the 1 million workers in its system use TopCoder to augment their income. However (and as we discussed in detail in Chapter 4), the top 10 percent can make a full-time living on the platform, instead of having a traditional job. The top 2 percent can make more money on TopCoder than they could working for a company.

Readers should familiarize themselves with these platforms. As we suggested, start with Fiverr and play around with a few projects. Learning how to use these platforms and potentially participate as a crowdsourcing expert will be invaluable experience in the coming years. Think of the crowdsourcing platforms as the organization of freelancers and experts available to serve in place of full-time workers as needed. Digital Labor will replace much of the white-collar workers' portfolio, but not all of it. Crowdsourcing will be one place where this residual white-collar work will get done.

The Experience Economy

As Digital Labor progresses in capability and scope, the impact on the jobs that white-collar workers perform will be profound. If workers are no longer spending time on the work that they used to do, then what will they spend their time on? If there is no answer to this in the enterprise, then the result is that people will lose their jobs. If there are answers that suggest that the freeing up of some time will allow white-collar workers to do more valuable things, then everyone wins. Like most things, this is not an either/or answer. It will be both.

The key to understanding the answer to the time question is the driving force of the Experience Economy. The Experience Economy elevates the value of time for workers and customers of service. What does this mean? Essentially, it means that people will start thinking more about their time when they make economic decisions. Time will be a valuable factor to consider.

For the employer who is buying time from its employees in the form of a salary or wage, consideration must be given to how that relationship will change over time. With Digital Labor progressions, employers should consider these questions:

- How much time do you need to buy?
- How much do you pay for that time?
- Can you leverage crowdsourcing and other on-demand time purchases?
- Are you fully leveraging an employee's highest skills and potential once some of his or her time is freed up from Digital Labor?

For the worker who is selling time to an employer, he or she must consider the value of the time to the employee as more and more work gets done by Digital Labor, by asking these questions:

- Do I have new areas that drive more value to the employer?
- Am I worth more or less as Digital Labor progresses?
- Can or should I look to leverage my expertise to crowdsourcing platforms to augment my income?

These are profound questions to be explored in the coming years, and they lead to the much larger question about how people spend their time in our society:

- Do you rent out your time for a job that is unfulfilling so that you can make money to pay the bills?
- If so, how long will this last, and is this even a good thing to do?
- What are the alternatives?

Looking at this from the customer side of the equation, businesses will see tremendous pressure from the market not to waste their time. Businesses that waste customers' time will soon find themselves with shrinking market shares and margins.

The answers to all of these questions will drive the design of new products and services and the structure of labor markets that support them. Most new products and services will be designed around digital platforms and will use human labor only when and where it makes sense. This also creates risk and opportunity for those vested in the current labor market (i.e., employees and employers).

There are so many variables that affect the timing and impact of the changes to the labor markets from Digital Labor. But one thing is for certain: things will change dramatically in the coming years. Employers will begin to question the need for the amount and types of workers that they need to operate their firm:

- Does Monday-to-Friday, 9-to-5 make sense in a digital 24/7 world?

- Should we use employees, contractors, outsourcing, or crowdsourcing?

- Are employees a net asset or a net liability? And how do you measure this?

Most companies we deal with are in the starting blocks in terms of answering these questions. In fact, many of them do not understand the issues outlined in this book well enough to even frame the questions for their firm.

So, while the rise of Digital Labor presents a huge existential risk to white-collar workers in the coming years, there is also a huge opportunity for those workers who are ready to adapt and take control of their time.

Flourishing in the Experience Economy

Workers who understand Digital Labor can avoid the coming demise of jobs if they are willing to adapt to the new business landscape. There are two essential ingredients required to succeed: attitude and aptitude. The most important one is attitude.

Attitude has to do with how you view the coming changes. The right attitude requires a level of curiosity and interest about how the emerging technology will impact every facet of business. There is an old saying, "People who are interested are interesting." Interesting people are attractive to other people and businesses alike and are more likely to be engaged for work.

Another aspect of attitude is a deep desire to learn new things and not be closed-minded about what is possible and what is not. Prior experiences must inform you, but not close you off to the possibility that things could change. A good attitude is one that is open to possibilities and a will to challenge the norms.

The second key ingredient is aptitude. You must have the ability to understand the technology and how it will impact the way things get done. You do not need to be a scientist or engineer, but you must be able to grasp the implications of the technology progression and how it will change the way things work. This is more of a strategic aptitude than a technical one.

For example, if AI chatbots can understand voice interaction and respond in a natural voice like the Google Duplex demonstration, what are the implications? Forget how the technology works—if it works, then what are the implications? It is not just about replacing call centers staffed by people. If Google Duplex works at scale, we have the opportunity to redesign many things that would have been too expensive or clumsy if you had to use human labor. Thinking outside of the box, we could use Google Duplex to do different things, such as listening to a boring 60-minute conference call and sending us the key highlights in an e-mail. During that hour, we could go for a swim and not waste time on the call *and* we would not miss anything because we blew it off.

Aptitude is more than having the ability to understand what is happening and think it through; there is also a creative element to aptitude. Being creative would include using Google Duplex to attend 3 to 4 of my meetings that are typically a waste of my time and do something more productive. Creativity comes in all shapes or forms and is intrinsically linked to attitude. Curiosity leads to creativity. Aptitude allows you to channel ideas into workable formats.

"What Happens to Me?"

I am often asked the question, "What happens to me?" or "What should I do?" when people become exposed to the concepts of Digital Labor.

The demise of the white-collar worker is coming. When, how fast, and the degree of the impact are debatable, but that does not mean that people cannot shift to new areas.

Here is a harsh reality: metaphorically speaking, the Digital Labor train is leaving the station and there are not enough seats on the train for everyone. Specifically, digitally based businesses do not need the number of white-collar workers that they have today—not even close.

However, to get on the Digital Labor train and flourish, you only need to buy a ticket—this essentially means that you must opt into the future. The price of the ticket is attitude and aptitude. My experience is that if anyone has trouble buying this ticket, it is because that person lacks the right attitude. This can be addressed as a matter of choice and self-reflection.

It is my deepest desire to convince as many people as I can to buy this metaphorical ticket. The more people who buy the ticket, the more likely that dystopian outcomes become utopian outcomes.

After all, what is the point of success if it is not shared broadly?

EPILOGUE:

Beyond Digital Labor

"The first step is to establish that something is possible; then probability will occur."

\- Elon Musk

VIRTUALLY EVERY FACET OF OUR LIVES, every organization, every field of study will be impacted by AI and Digital Labor technologies. White-collar labor involving the use of computers is just one field of many to be disrupted. We're seeing similar trends in everything from computer science to engineering, economics, politics, architecture, healthcare, and more, as shown in the graphic below.

The Digital Labor Neighborhood

Advanced technologies in almost every discipline are evolving in parallel, increasingly assuming responsibility for the more mundane tasks at work and at home. In the future, the beneficiaries of these technologies will have more time to consider larger issues, such as our purpose as human beings. Why are we here? What is our goal as a society? What should we aspire to do, collectively? And how do we become happy? AI will radically change how we live.

Our daily lives will continue to be rapidly transformed due to technology at an ever-increasing pace. The wireless computer in our pocket called a smartphone has changed the way we communicate and interact with the world. New digital businesses like Amazon, Netflix, Uber, and Facebook have changed the way we shop, consume television, use transportation, and socialize. The stage is set for more profound changes in the very near future.

That is our new reality, which will continue to be shaped in surprising ways by new technology. Some new developments are mind-blowing and similar to fantastical devices we've seen in science-fiction movies. Many are already in development today and on the cusp of being released.

Future Technology

In order to imagine the possibility of the coming changes to our businesses, our society, and the way we live, you need to have a cursory familiarity with some of the technologies in the word cloud shown above.

To describe each of these technologies, even briefly, would turn this epilogue into a book of its own. I've recorded many hours of podcasts diving deep into just the innovations affecting genomics alone.

Think about the world of science fiction becoming reality in the next 5 to 10 years and you can begin to imagine the changes that are coming to our economy, our society, our relationships, and who we are as people. These changes are going to be substantial and there is little that we can do to slow it down, which is causing many to be fearful.

At the heart of that fear is a lack of understanding of the various technologies that are shaping our world. The less people know about something new and disruptive, the more they tend to be fearful. This is the way humans have developed over time. In order to get past the fear, it is important to have some familiarity to better appreciate and plan for how emerging technologies will impact our lives.

Technology is neither good nor bad. It simply is, and the good or bad comes from how the technology is used. In order to understand how, when, and where emerging technology can be used, I encourage you to become more familiar with the areas that are of concern to you.

Let's consider Neuralink, founded by Elon Musk. Neuralink is a company developing new machine-brain interface (MBI) technology. The technology consists of microchips and an interconnected electrode array that are inserted into the brain. The array consists primarily of microscopic threads that weave throughout the brain's neuronal pathways. These fibers are injected using a robotic sewing machine, which Musk assures works within micron precision. Once implanted, through a combination of AI-based software that learns to understand the electrical signals of your brain and a biological function called neuroplasticity that allows the brain to adapt itself, the electrode array and the brain learn to communicate. It sounds crazy and you might be saying to yourself, "No chance am I doing that."

Neuralink's technology is amoral in that it is neither inherently good nor bad. We can imagine the ability of Neuralink to provide mobility to the paralyzed, communication to those afflicted with autism, or memory enhancement for those suffering with Alzheimer's disease. We can also easily imagine that some nefarious organization could manipulate thoughts of customers to the point of creating a human-based drone army. The utopian and dystopian are both possibilities, but it is the dystopian scenarios that capture our attention.

Technologies like Neuralink are exponentially disruptive and have the potential to change the way we interact with the world. They are a step towards the augmentation of human capabilities that extends beyond our own biological implications, even to the extent of calling into question where the line is between human and machine. The more we are aware of feats of this nature and their potential impact on our society, our economy, our social constructs, and our political systems, the more equipped we'll be to approach the design of any necessary adjustments to the policies that govern us.

At my management consultancy, we have numerous resources published at www.rumjog.com that discuss these issues in a way that is accessible to most people. We try to explain the implications of digital innovations in a way that is accessible to the lay person who may not have time to constantly study how AI is changing various industries. Another resource I use to keep up with technology trends is the website www.singularityhub.com, which is run by Singularity University. This website summarizes news and events from a variety of scientific and technology sources and is targeted for a general audience.

The more you understand these emerging trends, the more control you are likely retain in your personal and professional life. It is possible to pursue the utopian possibilities of digital disruption while evading or minimizing its more dystopian impacts. It is a choice, and to claim proud ignorance is to make a choice to be eventually swept up in the waves of invention that inevitably erode our shores of normalcy and status quo.

What Does It Mean to Be Human?

Humans are social, curious, naturally adaptive, and creative beings. Today, machines and software lack these qualities. We need to focus and pursue opportunities that leverage and enhance our human traits versus our attempts to do the repetitive work of machines. If humans try to compete with machines on machine terms, we will not fare well.

As Digital Labor restructures our society and our lives, one of the important questions for us as humans is to think about how we will spend our time once automation frees us from much of the tedious workload that has defined the 9-to-5 rat race of the past couple of centuries. Thinking about making a wise pivot to the future will make the difference between being freed by the machines with newfound time on our hands versus being displaced by the machines and worried about finding work, paying rent, and supporting a family.

For many people, this pivot will not be possible. Yes, there will be a net job loss, but new jobs focused on working with technology have been emerging to fill the gap, right? While this may be true, not every dog can learn new tricks. The gap between displaced workforces and their aggregate ability to shift into the new types of roles requiring new skills and training will be a significant figure, unfortunately. New roles are targeted for younger workers and less so on career veterans looking to make a switch. This inability to shift into new roles, as well as the net job loss from automation overall, is what much of my earlier analysis in this book has focused on.

However, for those who do successfully pivot, the story doesn't end there. The future of work will not only be different, but it will certainly be much less intensive, meaning more value per hour of work, and a focus on delivering outcomes versus punching the card for the allotted 40+ hours a week. The question remains, what will we do with all this time?

I believe we need to start by reflecting on what we truly value. As social, curious, creative beings, it's likely we'll find we value personal relationships, friendships, activities, new experiences, learning new skills, practicing crafts, and volunteering to support organizations and charities we admire. With less time required to work and provide for the necessities of life, we'll have much more time to devote to personal interests and global causes.

Maslow's Hierarchy of Needs

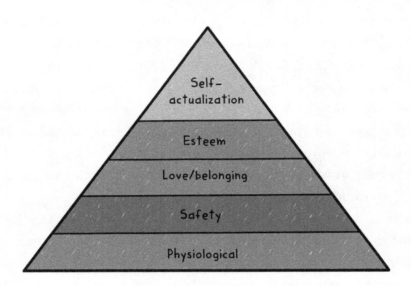

For many generations, according to Maslow's Hierarchy of Needs, we've been short-changing ourselves. Although there are five levels, or five needs, we've been so focused on basic physiological and safety needs that we haven't been able to progress and achieve substantial personal growth collectively. We've been consumed with surviving, maintaining a supply of food, clothing, and shelter for our families, and providing security and safety. Many have been stuck on those two lower, basic levels and only progress to worrying about higher goals when time allows, including love and belonging, esteem, and self-actualization. We haven't been fully living as human beings, Maslow would say.

And we may soon have that chance. For much of human history, most of our efforts and resources have gone to satisfying these base two layers of Maslow's hierarchy. Automation and Digital Labor will change this and make it much easier for individuals and societies to provide these basic needs. As a result, we will no longer need to obsess about clothing and feeding our children, or even maintaining our homes, because that will be taken care of.

We'll then have the chance to invest more energy into building and deepening our personal relationships with family and friends. We'll be able to be more social beings.

For those fortunate enough to be the beneficiaries of this change, you will then be given more freedom to strive and reach the top two layers, of esteem, or feel a sense of accomplishment, and self-actualization, or truly be our best selves. This shift in focus means a shift in what we value, as the top two layers have nothing to do with material possessions and job titles and status symbols and everything to do with making a difference in the world.

For those who ignore the coming changes and do not adapt, their future is much less promising, in stark contrast to those flourishing in the new and emerging economy. Increasingly, those who do not pivot will be reliant on others to provide the base layers of Maslow's hierarchy. This reliance can come from family or, more likely, from government and social assistance. This is hardly a fulfilling path or a path that leads to happiness.

In Maslow's world, happiness is defined by the height (not the width) of the hierarchical pyramid, or how close one can get to self-actualization. And it turns out that people who remain focused on those lower levels rarely feel a deep sense of happiness and belonging. They may be wealthy and able to accumulate plenty of belongings, but they can't achieve deep personal relationships or feel a sense of accomplishment for attaining a personal goal. Their pyramid is short and wide, rather than tall and thin, which is the ideal, according to Maslow. Happiness is vertical and materialism is horizontal.

The good news is that younger generations like the Millennials seem to get it. Millennials as a group are less likely to own things and more likely to invest in experiences. They are much less focused on acquisition and much more passionate about personal causes. And they're much less willing to put off happiness until later. Unlike older generations, they're not willing to wait until retirement to climb Mt. Everest or travel around the world or give all their money to charity.

We're already seeing this in how they prefer to work. They're much more likely to want to start businesses or participate in the gig economy than be tied to a corporate boss. They want freedom and independence more than they want a typical 9-to-5 job with promotions every year.

We all need to think more about what happiness looks like for us as individuals. What would it take to be truly happy? What change to your life would you need to make to be happier? What do you want to do less of? And what kinds of activities do you want to fill your days?

The pace of innovation is surpassing society's ability to pivot in tandem. We need to adapt now to ensure that automation, AI, and other digital technologies are embraced in ways that augment our species rather than in ways that cripple it. The decisions we make now will mean the difference between prosperity over poverty. They'll determine who will live lives of abundance versus lives of scarcity. These are technologies that can and will redefine all aspects of life as we know it, so it's a global discussion that everyone needs to participate in. And if we do get it right, we'll welcome in a new era of technological advancement that is boundless in its possibilities.

Acknowledgements

MANY YEARS WENT INTO the idea of writing of this book. However, turning an idea into a book is easier said than done. First and foremost, I want to thank Kiran Bajwa from our team here at Rumjog. One day she just started calling publishers and took control of the process to get this book from idea to reality.

As any author will admit, the experience is both internally challenging and rewarding. In addition, having to manage a business while writing certainly made this much tougher and longer than I was expecting, although it has also made the whole process more gratifying than I could have ever imagined. The ideas for this book stemmed from numerous white papers, lectures, presentations, etc., and I want to thank a number of people for helping me pull all the pieces together to turn them into a completed manuscript.

I want to thank the whole Rumjog team for all their efforts. Their comments, criticisms, ideas, and excitement during this project really helped me to put forward content that not only challenged our readers but also challenged me to improve and reinforce my own ideas and concepts. Beyond Bart Gallo, TJ Young, and Wendy Azevedo, I want to specifically thank Shawn Oommen for helping Kiran down the stretch and for driving our team to leverage the Microsoft Teams platform to collaborate on edits in the final months of the book development.

I want to thank;

- The Kevin Anderson Publishing team, for providing the publishing framework and being patient with us during the writing process;

- Marcia Layton Turner, who helped convert our ideas and draft into readable format. For believing in our vision and keeping me honest throughout the journey. During the preparation of this manuscript her enthusiasm and honesty helped to inform our approach throughout the creative process. Thanks for making sure our words and stories were connecting with our readers.

- Ruth Mills, our editor, who continuously helped to make sure we were delivering high quality content with fresh ideas. Her regular comments and suggestions during this project really helped to ensure consistency and readability of the book.

Without the experiences and support from the Rumjog team and the Kevin Anderson team, this process would have been way less enjoyable.

Finally, thank you to the countless individuals with who have shared concepts and helped me refine the ideas in this book, you gave inspiration to this process without even knowing it.

ENDNOTES

1 Liedtke, Michael and Mae Anderson, "Blockbuster Tries to Rewrite the Script in Bankruptcy," Boston.com, Sept. 23, 2010,
archive.boston.com/business/articles/2010/09/23/blockbuster_tries_to_rewrite_script_in_bankruptcy/

2 Toledo, Rob, "The Idea for Netflix Came from $40 in Late Fees on an 'Apollo 13' Rental," Extreamist, Oct. 8, 2015,
exstreamist.com/the-idea-for-netflix-came-from-40-in-late-fees-on-an-apollo-13-rental/

3 Hu, Cherie, "The Record Labels of the Future are Already Here," Forbes.com, Oct. 15, 2016,
forbes.com/sites/cheriehu/2016/10/15/the-record-labels-of-the-future-are-already-here/

4 Byrnes, Nanette, "As Goldman Embraces Automation, Even the Masters of the Universe are Threatened," MIT Technology Review, Feb. 7, 2017,
technologyreview.com/s/603431/as-goldman-embraces-automation-even-the-masters-of-the-universe-are-threatened

5 Simon, Matt, "Robots Wielding Water Knives are the Future of Farming," Wired.com, May 31, 2017, wired.com/2017/05/robots-agriculture/

6 Bhattacharyya, Suman, "Swedish Bank SEB is Using a 'Cognitive Agent' for Customer Service," Tearsheet, June 2, 2017,
tearsheet.co/modern-banking-experience/swedish-bank-seb-is-using-a-cognitive-agent-for-customer-service/

7 PwC, "Sizing the Prize: What's the real value of AI for your business and how can you capitalize?"

[8] Bureau of Labor Statistics, U.S. Department of Labor, Occupational Outlook Handbook, Bookkeeping, Accounting, and Auditing Clerks, bls.gov/ooh/office-and-administrative-support/bookkeeping-accounting-and-auditing-clerks.htm#tab-6

[9] Gallego, Jelor, "New Report Predicts Over 100,000 Legal Jobs Will be Lost to Automation," Futurism, March 23, 2016, futurism.com/new-report-predicts-over-100000-legal-jobs-would-be-lost-to-technological-automation

[10] Wakefield, Jane, "Foxconn Replaces '60,000 Factory Workers with Robots,'" BBC News, May 25, 2106, bbc.com/news/technology-36376966

[11] Sklar, Julia, "Robots Lay Three Times as Many Bricks as Construction Workers," MIT Technology Review, Sept. 2, 2015, technologyreview.com/s/540916/robots-lay-three-times-as-many-bricks-as-construction-workers/

[12] Feingold, Spencer, "Field of Machines: Researchers Grow Crop Using Only Automation," CNN, Oct. 7, 2017, cnn.com/2017/10/07/world/automated-farm-harvest-england/index.html

[13] Wisner, Matthew, "Former McDonald's USA CEO: Robots to Replace People in the Service Industry Going Forward," Fox Business, March 1, 2017, foxbusiness.com/features/former-mcdonalds-usa-ceo-robots-to-replace-people-in-the-service-industry-going-forward

[14] Clifford, Catherine, "9 of the Most Jaw-Dropping Things Elon Musk Said About Robots and AI in 2017," CNBC, Dec. 18, 2017, cnbc.com/2017/12/18/9-mind-blowing-things-elon-musk-said-about-robots-and-ai-in-2017.html

[15] Gray, Richard, "How Automation will Affect You – The Experts' View," BBC, May 23, 2017, bbc.com/future/story/20170522-how-automation-will-affect-you-the-experts-view

[16] Shead, Sam, "Amazon Now Has 45,000 Robots in its Warehouses," Business Insider, Jan. 3, 2017, businessinsider.com/amazons-robot-army-has-grown-by-50-2017-1

[17] Cipriani, Jason, "What is Google Duplex," CNET, May 24, 2018, cnet.com/how-to/what-is-google-duplex/

[18] Gent, Edd, "DeepMind's New AI Taught Itself to be the World's Greatest Go Player," SingularityHub, Oct. 23, 2017, singularityhub.com/2017/10/23/deepminds-new-ai-taught-itself-to-be-the-worlds-greatest-go-player

[19] Addison, Rebecca, "Uber Marks One-Year Anniversary of Driverless Car Launch," Pittsburgh City Paper, Sept. 20, 2017,

pghcitypaper.com/Blogh/archives/2017/09/20/uber-marks-one-year-anniversary-of-driverless-car-launch

[20] Bhuiyan, Johana, "Uber has published its much sought after diversity numbers for the first time," Vox, March 28, 2017,

vox.com/2017/3/28/15087184/uber-diversity-numbers-first-three-million

[21] Schleifer, Theodore, "Uber's Latest Valuation: $72 billion," Vox, Feb. 9, 2018,

vox.com/2018/2/9/16996834/uber-latest-valuation-72-billion-waymo-lawsuit-settlement

[22] Vincent, John M. and Cherise Threewitt, "How Do Those Car Insurance Tracking Devices Work?" US News & World Report, Feb. 26, 2018,

cars.usnews.com/cars-trucks/car-insurance/how-do-those-car-insurance-tracking-devices-work

[23] Knapp, Alex, "Gartner Estimates AI Business Value to Reach Nearly $4 Trillion by 2022," Forbes.com, April 25, 2018,

forbes.com/sites/alexknapp/2018/04/25/gartner-estimates-ai-business-value-to-reach-nearly-4-trillion-by-2022/

[24] Clifton, Jim, "The World's Broken Workplace," Gallup, June 13, 2017,

news.gallup.com/opinion/chairman/212045/world-broken-workplace.aspx